Adult
MAD LIBS®

World's Greatest Word Game

PARTY GIRL MAD LIBS

By Roger Price and Leonard Stern

PSS!
PRICE STERN SLOAN

W9-AHB-470

This 2008 edition of *Adult Mammoth Mad Libs* created
exclusively for Barnes & Noble Publishing, Inc. under ISBN-13: 978-0-8431-2328-9
and ISBN-10: 0-8431-2328-1.

ROADSIDE AMUSEMENTS
an imprint of
CHAMBERLAIN BROS.
Published by the Penguin Group
Price Stern Sloan, a division of Penguin Group for Young Readers.
Penguin Group (USA) Inc., 375 Hudson Street, New York, New York 10014, USA
Penguin Group (Canada), 10 Alcorn Avenue, Toronto, Ontario, Canada M4V 3B2
(a division of Pearson Penguin Canada Inc.)
Penguin Books Ltd, 80 Strand, London WC2R 0RL, England
Penguin Ireland, 25 St Stephen's Green, Dublin 2, Ireland (a division of Penguin Books Ltd)
Penguin Group (Australia), 250 Camberwell Road, Camberwell, Victoria 3124, Australia
(a division of Pearson Australia Group Pty Ltd)
Penguin Books India Pvt Ltd, 11 Community Centre, Panchsheel Park,
New Delhi–110 017, India
Penguin Group (NZ), Cnr Airborne and Rosedale Roads,
Albany, Auckland 1310, New Zealand (a division of Pearson New Zealand Ltd)
Penguin Books (South Africa) (Pty) Ltd, 24 Sturdee Avenue,
Rosebank, Johannesburg 2196, South Africa

Penguin Books Ltd, Registered Offices: 80 Strand, London WC2R 0RL, England

An application has been submitted to register this book with the Library of Congress.

ISBN 1-59609-149-5

Printed in the United States of America
2008 Printing

MAD LIBS®

INSTRUCTIONS

MAD LIBS® is a game for people who don't like games!
It can be played by one, two, three, four, or forty.

• RIDICULOUSLY SIMPLE DIRECTIONS

In this tablet you will find stories containing blank spaces where words are left out. One player, the **READER**, selects one of these stories. The **READER** does not tell anyone what the story is about. Instead, he/she asks the other players, the **WRITERS**, to give him/her words. These words are used to fill in the blank spaces in the story.

• TO PLAY

The **READER** asks each **WRITER** in turn to call out a word—an adjective or a noun or whatever the space calls for—and uses them to fill in the blank spaces in the story. The result is a **MAD LIBS®** game.

When the **READER** then reads the completed **MAD LIBS®** game to the other players, they will discover that they have written a story that is fantastic, screamingly funny, shocking, silly, crazy, or just plain dumb—depending upon which words each **WRITER** called out.

• EXAMPLE (*Before* and *After*)

"_____!" he said _____
      EXCLAMATION   ADVERB

as he jumped into his convertible _____ and
                                                          NOUN

drove off with his _____ wife.
                              ADJECTIVE

"_____*Ouch*_____!" he said _____*Stupidly*_____
      EXCLAMATION   ADVERB

as he jumped into his convertible _____*Cat*_____ and
                                                          NOUN

drove off with his _____*brave*_____ wife.
                              ADJECTIVE

MAD LIBS®
QUICK REVIEW

In case you have forgotten what adjectives, adverbs, nouns, and verbs are, here is a quick review:

An **ADJECTIVE** describes something or somebody. *Lumpy, soft, ugly, messy,* and *short* are adjectives.

An **ADVERB** tells how something is done. It modifies a verb and usually ends in "ly." *Modestly, stupidly, greedily,* and *carefully* are adverbs.

A **NOUN** is the name of a person, place, or thing. *Sidewalk, umbrella, bridle, bathtub,* and *nose* are nouns.

A **VERB** is an action word. *Run, pitch, jump,* and *swim* are verbs. Put the verbs in past tense if the directions say PAST TENSE. *Ran, pitched, jumped,* and *swam* are verbs in the past tense.

When we ask for **A PLACE**, we mean any sort of place: a country or city *(Spain, Cleveland)* or a room *(bathroom, kitchen).*

An **EXCLAMATION** or **SILLY WORD** is any sort of funny sound, gasp, grunt, or outcry, like *Wow!, Ouch!, Whomp!, Ick!,* and *Gadzooks!*

When we ask for specific words, like a **NUMBER**, a **COLOR**, an **ANIMAL**, or a **PART OF THE BODY**, we mean a word that is one of those things, like *seven, blue, horse,* or *head*.

When we ask for a **PLURAL**, it means more than one. For example, *cat* pluralized is *cats.*

MAD LIBS® is fun to play with friends, but you can also play it by yourself! To begin with, DO NOT look at the story on the page below. Fill in the blanks on this page with the words called for. Then, using the words you have selected, fill in the blank spaces in the story.

Now you've created your own hilarious MAD LIBS® game!

HIS HORRORSCOPE

PART OF THE BODY _____

ADJECTIVE _____

NOUN _____

VERB ENDING IN "ING" _____

NOUN _____

NOUN _____

ADJECTIVE _____

ADJECTIVE _____

ADJECTIVE _____

NOUN _____

ADJECTIVE _____

PART OF THE BODY _____

NOUN _____

ADJECTIVE _____

NOUN _____

PERSON IN ROOM _____

ADVERB _____

ADVERB _____

ADJECTIVE _____

MAD LIBS®
HIS HORRORSCOPE

As you take one last look at your _____ in the mirror,
PART OF THE BODY

you spy a copy of a/an _____ women's magazine on
ADJECTIVE

your coffee _____. You decide to read your date's
NOUN

horoscope for today. "Beware, Mercury is in retrograde. You will find

yourself _____ at work, but don't fly off the
VERB ENDING IN "ING"

_____. You could lose your _____. You are
NOUN   NOUN

in the _____ mood to take _____ chances
ADJECTIVE   ADJECTIVE

in your _____ life, but not until Venus realigns with
ADJECTIVE

its _____. Due to the _____ rash on your
NOUN   ADJECTIVE

_____, your love life is in the _____ for
PART OF THE BODY   NOUN

the next three months. A/An _____ person will come
ADJECTIVE

into your life and change your _____. Resist the urge
NOUN

to call _____ for help. You're bound to be
PERSON IN ROOM

_____ disappointed and _____
ADVERB   ADVERB

depressed." Maybe this date wasn't such a/an _____
ADJECTIVE

idea.

MAD LIBS® is fun to play with friends, but you can also play it by yourself! To begin with, DO NOT look at the story on the page below. Fill in the blanks on this page with the words called for. Then, using the words you have selected, fill in the blank spaces in the story.

Now you've created your own hilarious MAD LIBS® game!

THE CLOSET

NOUN _____

ADJECTIVE _____

ADJECTIVE _____

PLURAL NOUN _____

NOUN _____

ADJECTIVE _____

PLURAL NOUN _____

PART OF THE BODY (PLURAL) _____

PLURAL NOUN _____

PLURAL NOUN _____

NOUN _____

NOUN _____

Are you a party girl? Take this quiz and find out!

1. The best part of living in a party town like _____ is:
                                                    CITY

A. Increased chances of running into _____.
                                          CELEBRITY

B. Great transportation! It's easy to get around on subways and

_____.
  PLURAL NOUN

2. Have you ever stayed up all night _____ with your
                                      VERB ENDING IN "ING"

_____ even though you promised yourself you were
  PLURAL NOUN

going to _____ early that night?
          VERB

A. Um, I never _____ before midnight.
                 SAME VERB

B. I fall asleep as soon as my _____ hits the pillow.
                                PART OF THE BODY

3. The last time you _____ in on a Saturday night was:
                      VERB (PAST TENSE)

A. In the womb. Want _____ proof? Ask mom, she'll tell
                         ADJECTIVE

you I've been _____ since birth.
                 ADJECTIVE

B. I _____ every Saturday night!
     SAME VERB (PRESENT TENSE)

Answer: If you chose (b) for all the above, you need to get out more.

MAD LIBS® is fun to play with friends, but you can also play it by yourself! To begin with, DO NOT look at the story on the page below. Fill in the blanks on this page with the words called for. Then, using the words you have selected, fill in the blank spaces in the story.

Now you've created your own hilarious MAD LIBS® game!

DRINKING GUIDELINES

TYPE OF LIQUID _____

VERB ENDING IN "ING" _____

VERB ENDING IN "ING" _____

NOUN _____

ADJECTIVE_____

ADJECTIVE_____

ANIMAL _____

ADJECTIVE_____

PLURAL NOUN _____

VERB _____

NOUN _____

NOUN _____

PART OF THE BODY_____

NOUN _____

ADJECTIVE_____

NOUN _____

MAD LIBS®
DRINKING GUIDELINES

You and your friends all have signature cocktails, even though you'll

drink _____ if you have to. Here are a few and what
       TYPE OF LIQUID

they say about a person.

Beer: You're one of the guys, equally comfortable _____
                                    VERB ENDING IN "ING"

hot dogs at a ball game or _____ your hand in
                       VERB ENDING IN "ING"

Texas Hold 'Em.

Wine: A culture vulture, who likes to describe both _____
                                     NOUN

and wine as _____ and _____
        ADJECTIVE   ADJECTIVE

Martini: You're a lounge _____ who prowls the _____
               ANIMAL   ADJECTIVE

spots for sophisticated _____ to _____.
            PLURAL NOUN   VERB

Cosmopolitan: You're just a girly _____ who watches
                             NOUN

too many reruns of "_____ and the City"
               NOUN

Margarita: _____-loose and fancy free, you'll strip down
         PART OF THE BODY

to your _____ if encouraged.
      NOUN

Water: Healthy, _____ and well-hydrated, you're sure to
            ADJECTIVE

be popular . . . as the designated _____!
                          NOUN

MAD LIBS® is fun to play with friends, but you can also play it by yourself! To begin with, DO NOT look at the story on the page below. Fill in the blanks on this page with the words called for. Then, using the words you have selected, fill in the blank spaces in the story.

Now you've created your own hilarious MAD LIBS® game!

THE RIGHT PARTY LOOK

ADJECTIVE _____

CELEBRITY (FEMALE) _____

ADJECTIVE _____

PART OF THE BODY _____

ANIMAL _____

FOREIGN COUNTRY _____

COLOR _____

NOUN _____

ADVERB _____

PLURAL NOUN _____

ADJECTIVE _____

ADJECTIVE _____

ADJECTIVE _____

ADJECTIVE _____

PLURAL NOUN _____

NOUN _____

TYPE OF EVENT (PLURAL) _____

MAD LIBS®
THE RIGHT PARTY LOOK

We all have that one outfit that makes us feel _____
ADJECTIVE

and makes us look like _____ on her _____ day.
CELEBRITY (FEMALE)   ADJECTIVE

Soft hair: Strangers will want to run their _____
PART OF THE BODY

through it and pet it like their favorite _____
ANIMAL

Smoky eyes: Makes you look like you come from _____.
FOREIGN COUNTRY

Full _____ lips: Make every _____ in the place
COLOR   NOUN

want to kiss you _____
ADVERB

Soft hands: Every man wants to be caressed by the soft _____
PLURAL NOUN

of a/an _____ woman.
ADJECTIVE

Short skirt: Allows for a/an _____ imagination and very
ADJECTIVE

_____ thoughts.
ADJECTIVE

Shapely legs: Bound to make a/an _____ impression on
ADJECTIVE

all the leg _____ at the party.
PLURAL NOUN

Stilettos: Can be used as a/an _____ during _____
NOUN   TYPE OF EVENT (PLURAL)

MAD LIBS® is fun to play with friends, but you can also play it by yourself! To begin with, DO NOT look at the story on the page below. Fill in the blanks on this page with the words called for. Then, using the words you have selected, fill in the blank spaces in the story.

Now you've created your own hilarious MAD LIBS® game!

YOUR INTERNET PROFILE

ANIMAL _Dog_

PART OF THE BODY _Arm_

ADJECTIVE _Blue_

ADVERB ~~good~~ _quickly_

NOUN _Kitchen_

PLURAL NOUN _butt holes_

CELEBRITY (MALE) _George Clooey_

ADJECTIVE _purple_

NOUN _foot_

NOUN _floor_

ADJECTIVE _big_

NOUN _trees_

NOUN _bat_

PART OF THE BODY (PLURAL) _tits_

NOUN _Chair_

MAD LIBS®
YOUR INTERNET PROFILE

Why you should get to know me: I'm a cheeky _____
ANIMAL

who likes to party like a rock star. I have a gorgeous

_____ and a/an _____ wit.
PART OF THE BODY   ADJECTIVE

• Who I'm looking for: Someone who is _____
ADVERB

sophisticated who has traveled around the _____ and
NOUN

speaks many foreign _____. It won't hurt if he looks
PLURAL NOUN

like _____. But appearances aren't everything. He
CELEBRITY (MALE)

should also have a/an _____ bank account.
ADJECTIVE

• Three things I can't live without: A good _____ to read,
NOUN

my cell _____, and my _____ curiosity.
NOUN   ADJECTIVE

• Best (or worst) lie I've ever told: "I left my _____ in
NOUN

my other _____, officer!"
NOUN

• Place I wish I was right now: In the _____ of a
PART OF THE BODY (PLURAL)

loving _____.
NOUN

MAD LIBS® is fun to play with friends, but you can also play it by yourself! To begin with, DO NOT look at the story on the page below. Fill in the blanks on this page with the words called for. Then, using the words you have selected, fill in the blank spaces in the story.

Now you've created your own hilarious MAD LIBS® game!

L.A. PARTY

CITY _____

ADJECTIVE _____

NOUN _____

CELEBRITY (MALE) _____

SAME CITY _____

NUMBER _____

VERB _____

ROOM _____

ADJECTIVE _____

ARTICLE OF CLOTHING _____

TYPE OF CONTAINER _____

PLURAL NOUN _____

PART OF THE BODY (PLURAL) _____

OCCUPATION _____

PART OF THE BODY _____

COLOR _____

VERB _____

NUMBER _____

NUMBER _____

MAD LIBS®
L.A. PARTY

_____ Hilton just called with an invitation to that
    CITY

_____ party that's being thrown at Chez _____,
  ADJECTIVE   NOUN

the new restaurant owned by _____. _____
                                  CELEBRITY (MALE)   SAME CITY

says he's been asking for you and hopes you will be there tonight.

She says she'll pick you up in _____ minutes. You
                                       NUMBER

_____ to your _____, throw on your
  VERB   ROOM

_____ _____, and run out the door just as
  ADJECTIVE   ARTICLE OF CLOTHING

the limo is pulling up. You jump in and someone hands you a/an

_____ of champagne. As you pull up to the restaurant,
  TYPE OF CONTAINER

you see the paparazzi. They put their _____ up to their
                                   PLURAL NOUN

_____ and wait. The _____
  PART OF THE BODY (PLURAL)   OCCUPATION

opens the door, and you're the first one out. As you place one

_____ on the _____ carpet, the cameras
  PART OF THE BODY   COLOR

start flashing. You can't _____. You lose your step and
                        VERB

fall face first in front of _____ people. You didn't make
                      NUMBER

it into the party, but you did make Page _____.
                                      NUMBER

MAD LIBS® is fun to play with friends, but you can also play it by yourself! To begin with, DO NOT look at the story on the page below. Fill in the blanks on this page with the words called for. Then, using the words you have selected, fill in the blank spaces in the story.

Now you've created your own hilarious MAD LIBS® game!

FLIRTING 101

VERB _____

ADJECTIVE _____

NOUN _____

PART OF THE BODY _____

NOUN _____

PART OF THE BODY _____

ADJECTIVE _____

VERB _____

ADJECTIVE _____

NOUN _____

NOUN _____

PART OF THE BODY (PLURAL) _____

MAD LIBS®
FLIRTING 101

Flirting takes skill. It's not something you can _____
                                                    VERB

overnight. However, here are few tips to put you on your way to

becoming a/an _____ flirt.
                  ADJECTIVE

• When you spy a/an _____ to whom you are attracted,
                          NOUN

immediately make _____ contact. If possible, find a
                      PART OF THE BODY

mutual _____ who can introduce the two of you.
            NOUN

• Lightly touch his _____ while talking to him.
                        PART OF THE BODY

• Tell him that you think he's a/an _____ conversationalist.
                                        ADJECTIVE

• _____ out loud at his jokes even if they aren't _____.
      VERB   ADJECTIVE

• Always compliment him: the way he wears his _____
                                                      NOUN

or his beautiful speaking _____.
                              NOUN

• Be seductive without being obvious. Always swing your

_____ when you walk.
PART OF THE BODY (PLURAL)

From PARTY GIRL MAD LIBS® • Copyright © 2005 by Chamberlain Bros.,
a division of Penguin Group (USA), Inc., 375 Hudson Street, New York, New York 10014.

MAD LIBS® is fun to play with friends, but you can also play it by yourself! To begin with, DO NOT look at the story on the page below. Fill in the blanks on this page with the words called for. Then, using the words you have selected, fill in the blank spaces in the story.

Now you've created your own hilarious MAD LIBS® game!

SPEED DATING

ADJECTIVE_____

ADJECTIVE_____

NUMBER _____

NOUN _____

NUMBER _____

NOUN _____

ANIMAL _____

PART OF THE BODY_____

NOUN _____

ADJECTIVE_____

CELEBRITY (FEMALE)_____

TOWN_____

NUMBER _____

NOUN _____

VERB (PAST TENSE)_____

PART OF THE BODY (PLURAL) _____

NOUN _____

PERSON IN ROOM _____

NOUN _____

MAD LIBS®
SPEED DATING

You can't believe it's come to this: _____ dating. You're sitting
                                         ADJECTIVE

in this _____ restaurant and every _____
              ADJECTIVE   NUMBER

minutes, you move to another table to meet another _____.
                                                          NOUN

You've already met _____ jerks, and you have a/an _____
                         NUMBER   NOUN

in your stomach. The first one spoke as fast as a/an _____
                                                            ANIMAL

runs. The second wouldn't look you in the _____ and
                                                 PART OF THE BODY

kept scratching his _____. Next! The third guy was
                          NOUN

drop-dead _____. The problem? He looked like
                ADJECTIVE

_____. Now you're sitting across from a guy named
  CELEBRITY (FEMALE)

_____ who's wearing a jacket with _____
        TOWN   NUMBER

sleeves and a/an _____ on his head. "Haven't we _____
                      NOUN   VERB (PAST TENSE)

somewhere before?" You roll your _____ and check
                                       PART OF THE BODY (PLURAL)

your _____. It's seven. Time to get out of here, call
          NOUN

_____ and go grab a/an _____ to eat.
  PERSON IN ROOM   NOUN

From PARTY GIRL MAD LIBS® • Copyright © 2005 by Chamberlain Bros.,
a division of Penguin Group (USA), Inc., 375 Hudson Street, New York, New York 10014.

MAD LIBS® is fun to play with friends, but you can also play it by yourself! To begin with, DO NOT look at the story on the page below. Fill in the blanks on this page with the words called for. Then, using the words you have selected, fill in the blank spaces in the story.

Now you've created your own hilarious MAD LIBS® game!

GOOD GIRL...OR BAD?

PART OF THE BODY _____

ADJECTIVE _____

VERB _____

CELEBRITY (MALE) _____

PLURAL NOUN _____

ADJECTIVE _____

NOUN _____

VERB ENDING IN "ING" _____

ANIMAL _____

NOUN _____

ADVERB _____

NOUN _____

NOUN _____

MAD LIBS
GOOD GIRL...OR BAD?

It can feel so good to be bad. Do you tend to be more angel or vixen?

Take this little quiz and be honest (at least with yourself).

Would you:

• Wear a dress with a plunging _____-line to be
PART OF THE BODY

_____?
ADJECTIVE

• _____ a _____ on a first date?
    VERB   CELEBRITY MALE

• Take office _____ from work?
    PLURAL NOUN

• Spread _____ rumors about your friends?
    ADJECTIVE

• Return the leather _____ you found while _____
    NOUN   VERB ENDING IN "ING"

at the club?

• Drink like a/an _____?
    ANIMAL

• Light up a _____ even though you know it's
    NOUN

_____ dangerous?
ADVERB

• Bump into a parked _____ and leave a/an _____
    NOUN   NOUN

on the windshield?

From PARTY GIRL MAD LIBS® • Copyright © 2005 by Chamberlain Bros.,
a division of Penguin Group (USA), Inc., 375 Hudson Street, New York, New York 10014.

MAD LIBS® is fun to play with friends, but you can also play it by yourself! To begin with, DO NOT look at the story on the page below. Fill in the blanks on this page with the words called for. Then, using the words you have selected, fill in the blank spaces in the story.

Now you've created your own hilarious MAD LIBS® game!

A GIRL AND HER FRIENDS

ADJECTIVE_____

NOUN _____

ADVERB_____

VERB _____

PLURAL NOUN _____

NOUN _____

ADJECTIVE_____

ADJECTIVE_____

PLURAL NOUN _____

PART OF THE BODY_____

NOUN _____

ARTICLE OF CLOTHING_____

ADJECTIVE_____

SILLY NOISE _____

NOUN _____

NOUN _____

MAD LIBS
A GIRL AND HER FRIENDS

Every girl needs a few _____ girlfriends to hit the town
  ADJECTIVE

with. Friends who will stick by your side through thick or

_____. Friends who will _____ share the
  NOUN   ADVERB

check and not quibble over whose turn it is to _____ the
                                                VERB

next round. _____ you can call at the very last minute
              PLURAL NOUN

and be ready when you roll up in your convertible _____
                                                    NOUN

with a/an _____ invitation to a/an _____
            ADJECTIVE   ADJECTIVE

party. Friends you've known for many _____ , who have
                                        PLURAL NOUN

nursed you through a broken _____, cheered you when
                              PART OF THE BODY

you got that well deserved _____, and agreed that your
                             NOUN

designer _____ was a/an _____ steal. Most
          ARTICLE OF CLOTHING   ADJECTIVE

importantly, these friends know the type of guy you go

_____ over and won't think twice about approaching
  SILLY NOISE

someone who fits the description of your dream _____
                                                 NOUN

and asking, "What do you think of my _____ over there?"
                                       NOUN

MAD LIBS® is fun to play with friends, but you can also play it by yourself! To begin with, DO NOT look at the story on the page below. Fill in the blanks on this page with the words called for. Then, using the words you have selected, fill in the blank spaces in the story.

Now you've created your own hilarious MAD LIBS® game!

DISCO FEVER

CELEBRITY FEMALE _____

PART OF BODY _____

NOUN _____

NOUN _____

ADJECTIVE _____

ADJECTIVE _____

NOUN _____

VERB ENDING IN "ING" _____

VERB ENDING IN "ING" _____

ADVERB _____

ADVERB _____

PLURAL NOUN _____

PLURAL NOUN _____

PART OF BODY (PLURAL) _____

NOUN _____

NUMBER _____

ADJECTIVE _____

MAD LIBS
DISCO FEVER

You like to dance. Everyone knows it. It started when you saw

_____ shaking her _____ at a
CELEBRITY (FEMALE)   PART OF THE BODY

_____ event. You were hooked. So you decided to take
NOUN

_____ classes! They cost you a/an _____
NOUN   ADJECTIVE

fortune and every weekend you head to a/an _____
                                                          ADJECTIVE

night club and blow an arm and a/an _____ on cover
                                                NOUN

charges to practice _____. At first you are shy. You
                        VERB ENDING IN "ING"

start by _____ at the edge of the dance floor and
            VERB ENDING IN "ING"

_____ work your way to the center. You're
        ADVERB

_____ no longer shy. You're making all the right
        ADVERB

_____. A crowd gathers shouting _____ of
PLURAL NOUN   PLURAL NOUN

encouragement at the top of their _____. You love
                                      PART OF THE BODY (PLURAL)

it. You dance your _____ out. You take _____
                        NOUN   NUMBER

bows to _____ applause.
            ADJECTIVE

From PARTY GIRL MAD LIBS® • Copyright © 2005 by Chamberlain Bros.,
a division of Penguin Group (USA), Inc., 375 Hudson Street, New York, New York 10014.

MAD LIBS® is fun to play with friends, but you can also play it by yourself! To begin with, DO NOT look at the story on the page below. Fill in the blanks on this page with the words called for. Then, using the words you have selected, fill in the blank spaces in the story.

Now you've created your own hilarious MAD LIBS® game!

SPRING BREAK

ADJECTIVE _____

CITY _____

PLURAL NOUN _____

ADJECTIVE _____

NUMBER _____

PERSON IN ROOM _____

EXCLAMATION _____

NOUN _____

NOUN _____

NOUN _____

OCCUPATION _____

NOUN _____

VERB _____

MAD LIBS
SPRING BREAK

You and your friends have been saving for months for the ultimate

Spring Break vacation. After _____ discussions, you've all

ADJECTIVE

decided that _____ is the perfect place to party. You

CITY

spent weeks dreaming about all the hot _____ you

PLURAL NOUN

would meet, the _____ daiquiris you would consume,

ADJECTIVE

and how you wouldn't sleep for _____ days. You

NUMBER

booked the hotel online and were thrilled to find such a great rate.

But once you arrived, _____ took one look and

PERSON IN ROOM

exclaimed "_____! This place is a/an _____."

EXCLAMATION   NOUN

Undaunted, you decide to go down to the _____for a

NOUN

quick swim. But as soon as you open the door, the _____

NOUN

rings. It's the _____ telling you that there is a hundred

OCCUPATION

mile per hour _____ heading in your direction and that you

NOUN

might want to _____ as soon as possible. So much

VERB

for Spring Break.

MAD LIBS® is fun to play with friends, but you can also play it by yourself! To begin with, DO NOT look at the story on the page below. Fill in the blanks on this page with the words called for. Then, using the words you have selected, fill in the blank spaces in the story.

Now you've created your own hilarious MAD LIBS® game!

A DANGEROUS COCKTAIL

ADJECTIVE _____

PERSON IN ROOM _____

NOUN _____

NOUN _____

PLURAL NOUN _____

NOUN _____

NOUN _____

TYPE OF CONTAINER _____

ADVERB _____

NOUN _____

NOUN _____

ADJECTIVE _____

COLOR _____

SILLY NOISE _____

PERSON IN ROOM _____

ADJECTIVE _____

NOUN _____

MAD LIBS

A DANGEROUS COCKTAIL

It's your first time playing bartender and you're a little

_____. As a test, before _____ arrives,
       ADJECTIVE   PERSON IN ROOM

you decide to mix a _____ for yourself. Maybe it will
                              NOUN

become a smash at the _____ event. Maybe you'll go
                                NOUN

down in the history _____ as a beverage visionary. It
                           PLURAL NOUN

would definitely beat your day job in _____ sales. You
                                              NOUN

pick up the _____ juice and pour a generous amount
                    NOUN

into a/an _____ and shake it _____. Then
          TYPE OF CONTAINER   ADVERB

you add a sprig of _____ and a dash of _____.
                        NOUN   NOUN

Unexpectedly, at this point, it starts to bubble and turns a/an

_____ shade of _____. You make a/an
       ADJECTIVE   COLOR

_____ and quickly decide that _____ will
     SILLY NOISE   PERSON IN ROOM

tend bar tonight. So ends your short _____ life as a
                                             ADJECTIVE

_____-tender extraordinaire!
     NOUN

From PARTY GIRL MAD LIBS® • Copyright © 2005 by Chamberlain Bros.,
a division of Penguin Group (USA), Inc., 375 Hudson Street, New York, New York 10014.

MAD LIBS® is fun to play with friends, but you can also play it by yourself! To begin with, DO NOT look at the story on the page below. Fill in the blanks on this page with the words called for. Then, using the words you have selected, fill in the blank spaces in the story.

Now you've created your own hilarious MAD LIBS® game!

OFFICE PARTY OATH

ADJECTIVE _____

ADJECTIVE _____

VERB _____

PART OF THE BODY _____

NOUN _____

NOUN _____

ADJECTIVE _____

ARTICLE OF CLOTHING _____

NOUN _____

TYPE OF FOOD _____

SAME NOUN _____

A PLACE _____

ADJECTIVE _____

MAD LIBS

OFFICE PARTY OATH

Tonight is the _____ office Holiday party, and I do
<u>ADJECTIVE</u>

hereby promise that I will not make the same _____
<u>ADJECTIVE</u>

mistakes as last year. I will not _____ too much eggnog
<u>VERB</u>

and fall on my _____. When my boss wishes me
<u>PART OF THE BODY</u>

a Merry _____, I will not shout, "What am I? A
<u>NOUN</u>

_____-magnet?" I will not sniff near my boss's wife and
<u>NOUN</u>

ask her why she's marinating in such a/an _____
<u>ADJECTIVE</u>

perfume. I will not make photocopies of my _____
<u>ARTICLE OF CLOTHING</u>

and dance on the _____. I will not step in the
<u>NOUN</u>

_____ while dancing on the _____. I
<u>TYPE OF FOOD</u>   <u>SAME NOUN</u>

understand that it does not amuse my colleagues when I joke, "This

isn't an office, it's a/an _____ with fluorescent lighting!"
<u>A PLACE</u>

This year I promise I will be on my most _____
<u>ADJECTIVE</u>

behavior, because, for the love of Pete, I can't keep looking for a new

job every New Year's Day…

MAD LIBS® is fun to play with friends, but you can also play it by yourself! To begin with, DO NOT look at the story on the page below. Fill in the blanks on this page with the words called for. Then, using the words you have selected, fill in the blank spaces in the story.

Now you've created your own hilarious MAD LIBS® game!

THE WILDERNESS IS FOR THE BIRDS

ADJECTIVE _____

NOUN _____

NOUN _____

NOUN _____

COLOR _____

ANIMAL _____

EXCLAMATION _____

NOUN _____

NOUN _____

PART OF THE BODY _____

NOUN _____

SOMETHING ALIVE _____

NOUN _____

NOUN _____

VERB _____

NOUN _____

MAD LIBS®
THE WILDERNESS
IS FOR THE BIRDS

Your current date is passionate . . . about the _____

                                                ADJECTIVE

outdoors. Today, he's taking you hiking. You are wearing

_____ shoes and a comfortable _____.
     NOUN   NOUN

You're at the base of a mountain that looks as high as the Empire

_____ Building. You keep up for the first few minutes,
     NOUN

but then you start puffing and your face turns _____.
                                                 COLOR

Then you spy a/an _____ lurking in the bushes.
                          ANIMAL

"_____!" you yelp. You then rub against
  EXCLAMATION

_____ ivy and quickly get a nasty _____ on your
     NOUN   NOUN

leg. Your date starts to kiss your _____. This gives you
                                 PART OF THE BODY

the courage to go on. Finally, it's lunchtime and your date opens his

_____. He pulls out a/an _____ and a
     NOUN   SOMETHING ALIVE

thermos full of liquid _____. He expects you to put
                            NOUN

that in your _____? Is he crazy? You have no choice
               NOUN

but to _____, but you think to yourself, "This is the last
        VERB

time I commune with Mother _____."
                             NOUN

From PARTY GIRL MAD LIBS® • Copyright © 2005 by Chamberlain Bros.,
a division of Penguin Group (USA), Inc., 375 Hudson Street, New York, New York 10014.

MAD LIBS® is fun to play with friends, but you can also play it by yourself! To begin with, DO NOT look at the story on the page below. Fill in the blanks on this page with the words called for. Then, using the words you have selected, fill in the blank spaces in the story.

Now you've created your own hilarious MAD LIBS® game!

THE WISH LIST

ADJECTIVE _____

NOUN _____

TYPE OF BUILDING _____

NOUN _____

NOUN _____

OCCUPATION _____

NOUN _____

VERB _____

TOWN _____

NOUN _____

PART OF THE BODY _____

TYPE OF PLANT _____

VERB ENDING IN "ING" _____

TYPE OF LIQUID _____

ADJECTIVE _____

MAD LIBS®
THE WISH LIST

Whether we write it down or not, we all have a/an _____
ADJECTIVE

list of what we're looking for in the perfect mate. To wit:

- Loves his mother more than his new _____
  NOUN

- Can make rent every month on his _____
  TYPE OF BUILDING

- Isn't allergic to your pet _____
  NOUN

- Can speak _____ fluently
  NOUN

- Moonlights as a/an _____
  OCCUPATION

- Takes you to _____ games and likes to _____ you
  NOUN   VERB

- Watches old movies like "The Wizard of _____" and
  TOWN

"Gone with the _____"
  NOUN

- Adores your _____
  PART OF THE BODY

- Is careful about his health, sprinkling _____ in his
  TYPE OF PLANT

food and _____ to keep fit
  VERB ENDING IN "ING"

- Is careful about his appearance, slicking _____ in his
  TYPE OF LIQUID

hair and _____ lotion on his skin
  ADJECTIVE

From PARTY GIRL MAD LIBS® • Copyright © 2005 by Chamberlain Bros.,
a division of Penguin Group (USA), Inc., 375 Hudson Street, New York, New York 10014.

MAD LIBS® is fun to play with friends, but you can also play it by yourself! To begin with, DO NOT look at the story on the page below. Fill in the blanks on this page with the words called for. Then, using the words you have selected, fill in the blank spaces in the story.

Now you've created your own hilarious MAD LIBS® game!

THE SCAVENGER HUNT

ADJECTIVE _____

NOUN _____

PLURAL NOUN _____

NUMBER _____

PLURAL NOUN _____

PERSON IN ROOM _____

NOUN _____

OCCUPATION _____

NOUN _____

ARTICLE OF CLOTHING _____

ADJECTIVE _____

NOUN _____

ANIMAL _____

SMALL CITY _____

NOUN _____

VEHICLE _____

PLURAL NOUN _____

MAD LIBS®
THE SCAVENGER HUNT

Your friends are _____, so you've decided to have a
ADJECTIVE

scavenger hunt rather than go to the usual _____ for
NOUN

Friday-night _____. You've drawn up a list of things
PLURAL NOUN

to gather and plan on giving _____ _____
NUMBER   PLURAL NOUN

to the victor. _____ is the first to return and she/he
PERSON IN ROOM

has found everything, including:

• A digital photo of a/an _____
NOUN

• A business card from a/an _____
OCCUPATION

• A phone number written on a/an _____
NOUN

• A/An _____ from some _____ restaurant
ARTICLE OF CLOTHING   ADJECTIVE

• A/An _____ from a strip club
NOUN

• A live _____ from _____
ANIMAL   SMALL CITY

• A ticket stub from a/an _____ concert
NOUN

• A toy _____
VEHICLE

• A box of used _____
PLURAL NOUN

From PARTY GIRL MAD LIBS® • Copyright © 2005 by Chamberlain Bros.,
a division of Penguin Group (USA), Inc., 375 Hudson Street, New York, New York 10014.

MAD LIBS® is fun to play with friends, but you can also play it by yourself! To begin with, DO NOT look at the story on the page below. Fill in the blanks on this page with the words called for. Then, using the words you have selected, fill in the blank spaces in the story.

Now you've created your own hilarious MAD LIBS® game!

NEW YEAR'S EVE

ADJECTIVE _____

HOLIDAY _____

NOUN _____

NOUN _____

ADJECTIVE _____

CELEBRITY (FEMALE) _____

ADJECTIVE _____

NUMBER _____

ADJECTIVE _____

NOUN _____

NOUN _____

NUMBER _____

PERSON IN THE ROOM _____

FOREIGN COUNTRY _____

NOUN _____

NOUN _____

MAD LIBS®
NEW YEAR'S EVE

So many choices, but only one night! After the _____
ADJECTIVE

_____ you just spent with your _____,
HOLIDAY   NOUN

you're ready to let a little _____ off. The invites you've
NOUN

received so far are:

• A/An _____ party at the home of a _____
ADJECTIVE   CELEBRITY (FEMALE)

look alike

• A/An _____ invitation to go out with your Ex whom
ADJECTIVE

you haven't seen in _____ years but still have feelings
NUMBER

for occasionally

• A/An _____ cousin and her _____
ADJECTIVE   NOUN

think they have the perfect intimate party: a/an _____
NOUN

cooked dinner for _____ of their closest friends
NUMBER

But you're thinking that maybe you'll surprise _____
PERSON IN ROOM

who's visiting _____ and hop a jet _____
FOREIGN COUNTRY   NOUN

in time to have a quick _____ and ring in the New Year!
NOUN

MAD LIBS® is fun to play with friends, but you can also play it by yourself! To begin with, DO NOT look at the story on the page below. Fill in the blanks on this page with the words called for. Then, using the words you have selected, fill in the blank spaces in the story.

Now you've created your own hilarious MAD LIBS® game!

THE BLIND DATE

PERSON IN ROOM _____

NAME OF PERSON (MALE) _____

ADJECTIVE _____

ADJECTIVE _____

TYPE OF SPORT _____

OCCUPATION _____

OCCUPATION _____

CELEBRITY (FEMALE) _____

PUBLIC EVENT _____

VERB _____

TYPE OF BUILDING _____

TYPE OF EVENT _____

A PLACE _____

TYPE OF PLANT _____

VERB _____

NUMBER _____

ADJECTIVE _____

COLOR _____

PART OF THE BODY _____

VERB _____

_____ has fixed you up with _____. It's
PERSON IN ROOM   NAME OF PERSON (MALE)

your very first blind date and frankly, you're _____.
                                               ADJECTIVE

You haven't seen a picture of him but he's been described as

_____ and is on a/an _____ team. After a
ADJECTIVE   TYPE OF SPORT

stint as a/an _____, he settled into his current job as
             OCCUPATION

a/an _____. He's worked with _____ on
     OCCUPATION   CELEBRITY (FEMALE)

a charity _____ and apparently _____
          PUBLIC EVENT   VERB

with her at her country _____. You're hoping it works
                        TYPE OF BUILDING

out so you can hang with her at the next _____. He
                                         TYPE OF EVENT

shows up at your _____ with a large _____
                 A PLACE   TYPE OF PLANT

in hand. Unfortunately, it's not big enough to _____
                                               VERB

him. He weighs _____ pounds, has a/an _____
               NUMBER   ADJECTIVE

tooth, and a/an _____ blemish on the end of his
                COLOR

_____. Oh well, you can always close your eyes
PART OF THE BODY

when you _____ him later. That's why they are called
         VERB

blind dates.

MAD LIBS® is fun to play with friends, but you can also play it by yourself! To begin with, DO NOT look at the story on the page below. Fill in the blanks on this page with the words called for. Then, using the words you have selected, fill in the blank spaces in the story.

Now you've created your own hilarious MAD LIBS® game!

SOCIAL COORDINATOR

ADVERB _____

PLURAL NOUN _____

PLURAL NOUN _____

ADJECTIVE _____

NOUN _____

VERB _____

ADJECTIVE _____

VERB _____

NUMBER _____

CELEBRITY (MALE) _____

ANIMAL _____

HOLIDAY _____

CELEBRITY (FEMALE) _____

CELEBRITY (FEMALE) _____

NOUN _____

NUMBER _____

PLURAL NOUN _____

MAD LIBS®
SOCIAL COORDINATOR

Is it your fault you're so _____ popular? Of course all
                              ADVERB

of your _____ look to you to fill their _____
         PLURAL NOUN   PLURAL NOUN

with _____ and adventure. Problem is you're running
      ADJECTIVE

out of ideas! Your title of "Miss _____ U.S.A." is being
                                   NOUN

threatened, and you've got to _____ fast. But what
                               VERB

more could you do? You've already scored V.I.P. tickets to that

_____ concert featuring the band _____
   ADJECTIVE   VERB

_____. You convinced _____ to sneak
   NUMBER   CELEBRITY (MALE)

you into the _____ Club for a private party. You were
              ANIMAL

invited to the _____ party that _____
                HOLIDAY   CELEBRITY (FEMALE)

threw with _____. Both _____ magazine
            CELEBRITY (FEMALE)   NOUN

and Page _____ have cited you as the new It Girl, and
          NUMBER

even Joan _____ says you have excellent style.
           PLURAL NOUN

Maybe you should take a night off and let them fend for

themselves....

Adult

MAD LIBS

World's Greatest Word Game

TEST YOUR RELATIONSHIP IQ MAD LIBS

By Roger Price and Leonard Stern

PSS!
PRICE STERN SLOAN

ROADSIDE AMUSEMENTS
an imprint of
CHAMBERLAIN BROS.
Published by the Penguin Group
Price Stern Sloan, a division of Penguin Group for Young Readers.
Penguin Group (USA) Inc., 375 Hudson Street, New York, New York 10014, USA
Penguin Group (Canada), 10 Alcorn Avenue, Toronto, Ontario, Canada M4V 3B2
(a division of Pearson Penguin Canada Inc.)
Penguin Books Ltd, 80 Strand, London WC2R 0RL, England
Penguin Ireland, 25 St Stephen's Green, Dublin 2, Ireland (a division of Penguin Books Ltd)
Penguin Group (Australia), 250 Camberwell Road, Camberwell, Victoria 3124, Australia
(a division of Pearson Australia Group Pty Ltd)
Penguin Books India Pvt Ltd, 11 Community Centre, Panchsheel Park,
New Delhi–110 017, India
Penguin Group (NZ), Cnr Airborne and Rosedale Roads,
Albany, Auckland 1310, New Zealand (a division of Pearson New Zealand Ltd)
Penguin Books (South Africa) (Pty) Ltd, 24 Sturdee Avenue,
Rosebank, Johannesburg 2196, South Africa

Penguin Books Ltd, Registered Offices: 80 Strand, London WC2R 0RL, England

An application has been submitted to register this book with the Library of Congress.

ISBN 1-59609-151-7

Printed in the United States of America

PSS! and MAD LIBS are registered trademarks of Penguin Group (USA) Inc.

MAD LIBS®
INSTRUCTIONS

MAD LIBS® is a game for people who don't like games!
It can be played by one, two, three, four, or forty.

• RIDICULOUSLY SIMPLE DIRECTIONS

In this tablet you will find stories containing blank spaces where words are
left out. One player, the **READER**, selects one of these stories. The **READER**
does not tell anyone what the story is about. Instead, he/she asks the other
players, the **WRITERS**, to give him/her words. These words are used to fill
in the blank spaces in the story.

• TO PLAY

The **READER** asks each **WRITER** in turn to call out a word—an adjective or
a noun or whatever the space calls for—and uses them to fill in the blank
spaces in the story. The result is a **MAD LIBS®** game.

When the **READER** then reads the completed **MAD LIBS®** game to the other
players, they will discover that they have written a story that is fantastic,
screamingly funny, shocking, silly, crazy, or just plain dumb—depending
upon which words each **WRITER** called out.

• EXAMPLE (*Before* and *After*)

"_____ !" he said _____
         EXCLAMATION   ADVERB

as he jumped into his convertible _____ and
                                                    NOUN

drove off with his _____ wife.
                            ADJECTIVE

"_____*Ouch*_____ !" he said _____*stupidly*_____
         EXCLAMATION   ADVERB

as he jumped into his convertible _____*cat*_____ and
                                                    NOUN

drove off with his _____*brave*_____ wife.
                            ADJECTIVE

MAD LIBS
QUICK REVIEW

In case you have forgotten what adjectives, adverbs, nouns, and verbs are, here is a quick review:

An **ADJECTIVE** describes something or somebody. *Lumpy, soft, ugly, messy,* and *short* are adjectives.

An **ADVERB** tells how something is done. It modifies a verb and usually ends in "ly." *Modestly, stupidly, greedily,* and *carefully* are adverbs.

A **NOUN** is the name of a person, place, or thing. *Sidewalk, umbrella, bridle, bathtub,* and *nose* are nouns.

A **VERB** is an action word. *Run, pitch, jump,* and *swim* are verbs. Put the verbs in past tense if the directions say PAST TENSE. *Ran, pitched, jumped,* and *swam* are verbs in the past tense.

When we ask for **A PLACE**, we mean any sort of place: a country or city *(Spain, Cleveland)* or a room *(bathroom, kitchen).*

An **EXCLAMATION** or **SILLY WORD** is any sort of funny sound, gasp, grunt, or outcry, like *Wow!, Ouch!, Whomp!, Ick!,* and *Gadzooks!*

When we ask for specific words, like a **NUMBER**, a **COLOR**, an **ANIMAL**, or a **PART OF THE BODY**, we mean a word that is one of those things, like *seven, blue, horse,* or *head.*

When we ask for a **PLURAL**, it means more than one. For example, *cat* pluralized is *cats.*

MAD LIBS® is fun to play with friends, but you can also play it by yourself! To begin with, DO NOT look at the story on the page below. Fill in the blanks on this page with the words called for. Then, using the words you have selected, fill in the blank spaces in the story.

Now you've created your own hilarious MAD LIBS® game!

ARE YOU TRULY COMPATIBLE?

VERB _____

ADJECTIVE _____

ADJECTIVE _____

NOUN _____

ADJECTIVE _____

PLURAL NOUN _____

NOUN _____

VERB ENDING IN "ING" _____

VERB _____

ADJECTIVE _____

NOUN _____

ADJECTIVE _____

ADJECTIVE _____

TYPE OF LIQUID _____

VERB _____

ADJECTIVE _____

MAD LIBS

ARE YOU TRULY COMPATIBLE?

Sure, opposites _____, but you and your _____
                     VERB   ADJECTIVE

man still need to be compatible. Take this _____ quiz
                                                  ADJECTIVE

to see if he's the yin to your _____.
                                      NOUN

Which scenario best matches your _____ Friday night?
                                         ADJECTIVE

(a) He hangs out with his _____, while you stay home
                              PLURAL NOUN

and read a/an _____. Then, on Saturday, you spend all
                    NOUN

day _____ together.
      VERB ENDING IN "ING"

(b) You whine and ask him to _____ between you and
                                    VERB

his friends.

(c) You argue. He says you're _____ for wanting to stay
                                    ADJECTIVE

in your _____ all night and he pressures you into going
             NOUN

to a/an _____ event.
             ADJECTIVE

(d) You stay home. You rent a/an _____ romantic
                                        ADJECTIVE

comedy and pour yourself a glass of _____, while he
                                          TYPE OF LIQUID

plays _____-station 2 all night.
            VERB

Answer: (a) or (c) isn't too _____.
                                  ADJECTIVE

From TEST YOUR RELATIONSHIP IQ MAD LIBS® • Copyright © 2005 by Chamberlain Bros.,
a division of Penguin Group (USA), Inc., 375 Hudson Street, New York, New York 10014.

MAD LIBS® is fun to play with friends, but you can also play it by yourself! To begin with, DO NOT look at the story on the page below. Fill in the blanks on this page with the words called for. Then, using the words you have selected, fill in the blank spaces in the story.

Now you've created your own hilarious MAD LIBS® game!

IS HE REALLY COMMITTED?

ADJECTIVE_____

VERB _____

PLURAL NOUN _____

ADJECTIVE_____

NOUN _____

PART OF THE BODY _____

VERB _____

PLURAL NOUN _____

NOUN _____

EXCLAMATION_____

ADJECTIVE_____

NOUN _____

PLURAL NOUN _____

ADJECTIVE_____

VERB _____

MAD LIBS
IS HE REALLY COMMITTED?

Commitment makes some men feel pretty _____. If
ADJECTIVE

they start to _____ intimacy, they turn into
VERB

_____. Take this _____ quiz to figure
PLURAL NOUN   ADJECTIVE

out if he's in it for the long _____ . . . or if he has one
NOUN

_____ out the door.
PART OF THE BODY

When you ask him to _____ your parents, he:
VERB

(a) Claims he has front row_____ to the
PLURAL NOUN

_____ game for that night.
NOUN

(b) Says, "_____! Why?"
EXCLAMATION

(c) Looks at you with _____ eyes and says it would be
ADJECTIVE

a/an _____ to meet them.
NOUN

(d) Starts packing his _____.
PLURAL NOUN

Answer: This one doesn't count. Your parents are a little too

_____ to introduce him to, anyway, especially if you
ADJECTIVE

don't want to _____ him off.
VERB

From TEST YOUR RELATIONSHIP IQ MAD LIBS® • Copyright © 2005 by Chamberlain Bros.,
a division of Penguin Group (USA), Inc., 375 Hudson Street, New York, New York 10014.

MAD LIBS® is fun to play with friends, but you can also play it by yourself! To begin with, DO NOT look at the story on the page below. Fill in the blanks on this page with the words called for. Then, using the words you have selected, fill in the blank spaces in the story.

Now you've created your own hilarious MAD LIBS® game!

HOW TO RAISE YOUR I.Q.: NUMBER 1

NUMBER _____

VERB _____

ADJECTIVE_____

ADJECTIVE_____

VERB _____

PART OF THE BODY (PLURAL) _____

PART OF THE BODY (PLURAL) _____

ADJECTIVE_____

ADVERB_____

ADJECTIVE_____

NOUN _____

PART OF THE BODY _____

SAME PART OF THE BODY_____

VERB _____

ADJECTIVE_____

MAD LIBS
HOW TO RAISE YOUR I.Q.: NUMBER 1

You haven't had a date in _____ months. Don't
                                    NUMBER

_____ . You just need some _____
            VERB   ADJECTIVE

pointers to raise your relationship I.Q.

• When arriving at a/an _____ party, be the first to
                                 ADJECTIVE

_____ into the room. This way, all _____
         VERB   PART OF THE BODY (PLURAL)

are on you.

• Be relaxed. Keep your _____ at your sides
                            PART OF THE BODY (PLURAL)

especially when you're speaking to a/an _____ guy.
                                                ADJECTIVE

You don't want him to think you're _____ nervous.
                                            ADVERB

• "Mirroring" is a/an _____ technique. While talking to that
                          ADJECTIVE

special _____, you should note the position of his
              NOUN

_____, then rearrange your own _____
   PART OF THE BODY   SAME PART OF THE BODY

in the same manner.

• When in doubt, _____! A/an _____ smile
                        VERB   ADJECTIVE

will always attract admirers.

MAD LIBS® is fun to play with friends, but you can also play it by yourself! To begin with, DO NOT look at the story on the page below. Fill in the blanks on this page with the words called for. Then, using the words you have selected, fill in the blank spaces in the story.

Now you've created your own hilarious MAD LIBS® game!

IS HE CHEATING ON YOU?

NOUN _____

PLURAL NOUN _____

ADJECTIVE_____

ADJECTIVE_____

NOUN _____

ARTICLE OF CLOTHING_____

TYPE OF FURNITURE _____

NOUN _____

NOUN _____

NOUN _____

MAD LIBS®
IS HE CHEATING ON YOU?

Your sweetie has been a little distant lately, and you've been

wondering if he's a total _____ or a true blue fella.

NOUN

Answer true or false to the following _____ to see if

PLURAL NOUN

he's being faithful.

True or False

1) More than once he's cancelled a/an _____ date with

ADJECTIVE

you claiming a/an _____ emergency at the _____

ADJECTIVE NOUN

came up!

2) You find a pair of women's _____ under the

ARTICLE OF CLOTHING

_____—and they can't be yours, because you never

TYPE OF FURNITURE

wear any.

3) He says he's going to play a round of _____ with the

NOUN

guys, but when you follow him disguised as a/an _____,

NOUN

you see him at a poker _____ instead.

NOUN

If you answered True to (3), you might want to stop stalking the guy.

MAD LIBS® is fun to play with friends, but you can also play it by yourself! To begin with, DO NOT look at the story on the page below. Fill in the blanks on this page with the words called for. Then, using the words you have selected, fill in the blank spaces in the story.

Now you've created your own hilarious MAD LIBS® game!

IS HE YOUR SOUL MATE?

ADJECTIVE_____

PLURAL NOUN _____

VERB (PAST TENSE)_____

PART OF THE BODY (PLURAL) _____

NOUN _____

EXCLAMATION_____

NOUN _____

PART OF THE BODY_____

NOUN _____

ANIMAL _____

TYPE OF LIQUID _____

ANIMAL (PLURAL) _____

VERB ENDING IN "ING" _____

VERB _____

ADVERB_____

MAD LIBS

IS HE YOUR SOUL MATE?

If you believe in the _____ idea of soul

ADJECTIVE

_____, you'd better decide whether this romance is

PLURAL NOUN

really written in the stars.

Which best describes how you _____for the first time?

VERB (PAST TENSE)

(a) When your _____ met across a crowded

PART OF THE BODY (PLURAL)

_____, he made his way over and whispered

NOUN

"_____! You are one hot _____!" into

EXCLAMATION   NOUN

your _____.

PART OF THE BODY

(b) You met at a/an _____, where you both ordered

NOUN

_____ sandwiches with no crusts and a bottle of

ANIMAL

_____to go. Coincidence, or fate?

TYPE OF LIQUID

(c) The leashes of your _____were intertwined when

ANIMAL (PLURAL)

you were_____at a corner, and you've been inseperable

VERB ENDING IN "ING"

ever since.

Answer: If you met your man in any of these situations,

_____ him— _____!

VERB   ADVERB

From TEST YOUR RELATIONSHIP IQ MAD LIBS® • Copyright © 2005 by Chamberlain Bros.,
a division of Penguin Group (USA), Inc., 375 Hudson Street, New York, New York 10014.

MAD LIBS® is fun to play with friends, but you can also play it by yourself! To begin with, DO NOT look at the story on the page below. Fill in the blanks on this page with the words called for. Then, using the words you have selected, fill in the blank spaces in the story.

Now you've created your own hilarious MAD LIBS® game!

SHOULD YOU DUMP HIM?

NOUN _____

ADJECTIVE _____

VERB _____

NUMBER _____

NOUN _____

NUMBER _____

PLURAL NOUN _____

PLURAL NOUN _____

PART OF THE BODY _____

ADJECTIVE _____

NOUN _____

VERB _____

MAD LIBS
SHOULD YOU DUMP HIM?

We know being single can be awful, but there comes a time when

you have to throw in the _____ on a/an _____
                            NOUN   ADJECTIVE

relationship. Take this quiz to figure out if you need to

_____ this guy and/or move on.
        VERB

When you think of your boyfriend you:

(a) Remember the _____ dollars he owes you from the
                        NUMBER

time he desperately needed to fix his _____. (This
                                              NOUN

was _____ months ago.)
        NUMBER

(b) Think of his hot best friend, the one who always wears tight

_____ to show off his _____.
   PLURAL NOUN   PLURAL NOUN

(c) Cry. Your _____ was upset last night and he didn't
                 PART OF THE BODY

come by like he promised.

(d) Feel all warm and _____ when picturing him on your
                          ADJECTIVE

first date, but then you remember the icky _____ on his neck.
                                                  NOUN

Answer: If you chose any of the above you need to _____
                                                            VERB

this guy and be a single chick again for awhile.

MAD LIBS® is fun to play with friends, but you can also play it by yourself! To begin with, DO NOT look at the story on the page below. Fill in the blanks on this page with the words called for. Then, using the words you have selected, fill in the blank spaces in the story.

Now you've created your own hilarious MAD LIBS® game!

IS HE PULLING AWAY?

ADJECTIVE_____

VERB ENDING IN "ING" _____

ADJECTIVE_____

PLURAL NOUN _____

ADJECTIVE_____

NOUN _____

VERB _____

ADJECTIVE_____

COLOR_____

TYPE OF LIQUID _____

PART OF THE BODY (PLURAL) _____

VERB ENDING IN "ING" _____

PART OF THE BODY_____

LANGUAGE _____

VERB _____

ADVERB_____

MAD LIBS
IS HE PULLING AWAY?

As much as we'd like to deny it, _____ love doesn't
                                        ADJECTIVE

always last forever. Do you feel him _____ interest in
                                        VERB ENDING IN "ING"

you? Take this _____ quiz to find out he's ready to call
                    ADJECTIVE

it _____ . . . or if he's just in a/an _____ mood.
        PLURAL NOUN   ADJECTIVE

You suggest planning a trip to a foreign _____. He:
                                                NOUN

(a) Starts to squirm and _____ in his seat, saying how
                                VERB

his schedule tends to be really_____ that time of year.
                                        ADJECTIVE

(b) Asks if you want red or _____ _____
                                COLOR   TYPE OF LIQUID

with your pasta.

(c) Wrings his _____, claiming he's afraid of
                    PART OF THE BODY (PLURAL)

_____. When the plane reaches high altitudes
        VERB ENDING IN "ING"

his _____ bleeds.
        PART OF THE BODY

(d) Suggests you start taking _____ next week so that
                                    LANGUAGE

you can _____ with the locals.
                VERB

Answer: If (d) is his reply, book your flight_____, if
                                                    ADVERB

not sooner.

From MAD LIBS® TEST YOUR RELATIONSHIP IQ • Copyright © 2005 by Chamberlain Bros.,
a division of Penguin Group (USA), Inc., New York, 375 Hudson Street, New York, New York 10014.

MAD LIBS® is fun to play with friends, but you can also play it by yourself! To begin with, DO NOT look at the story on the page below. Fill in the blanks on this page with the words called for. Then, using the words you have selected, fill in the blank spaces in the story.

Now you've created your own hilarious MAD LIBS® game!

HOW TO RAISE YOUR I.Q.: NUMBER 2

NOUN _____

VERB ENDING IN "ING" _____

NOUN _____

PLURAL NOUN _____

NOUN _____

ADJECTIVE_____

ARTICLE OF CLOTHING_____

PLURAL NOUN _____

NOUN _____

NOUN _____

A PLACE _____

PLURAL NOUN _____

VERB _____

PLURAL NOUN _____

NOUN _____

NOUN _____

NOUN _____

MAD LIBS®
HOW TO RAISE YOUR I.Q.: NUMBER 2

You've mastered the art of _____ Language, but you're
                                    NOUN

still _____ at home on a Saturday night, watching
      VERB ENDING IN "ING"

T.V., eating junk _____ and wondering why you can't
                          NOUN

meet a guy like that hunk on *Desperate* _____.
                                                    PLURAL NOUN

Well, sister, put down that _____, and put on your
                                    NOUN

_____ _____. You're going out!
      ADJECTIVE   ARTICLE OF CLOTHING

• Scan the internet to find groups who are dedicated to the same

_____ you are.
      PLURAL NOUN

• If you have ever wanted to learn how to _____, how
                                                  NOUN

about taking a beginner's _____ at the local _____.
                                  NOUN   A PLACE

• Ask your _____ about groups or events they are
                  PLURAL NOUN

involved in then ask to _____ along.
                              VERB

• Organize a monthly "_____ Night Out" with all the
                              PLURAL NOUN

ladies listed in your personal _____.
                                        NOUN

Remember—nobody ever found the _____ of their
                                            NOUN

dreams by staying at home night after _____!
                                              NOUN

MAD LIBS® is fun to play with friends, but you can also play it by yourself! To begin with, DO NOT look at the story on the page below. Fill in the blanks on this page with the words called for. Then, using the words you have selected, fill in the blank spaces in the story.

Now you've created your own hilarious MAD LIBS® game!

DOES HE FLIRT TOO MUCH?

ADJECTIVE_____

VERB _____

ADJECTIVE_____

NOUN _____

A PLACE _____

ADJECTIVE_____

PART OF THE BODY _____

ADJECTIVE_____

PART OF THE BODY _____

ADJECTIVE_____

ADJECTIVE_____

NUMBER _____

TYPE OF LIQUID _____

VERB _____

ADJECTIVE_____

MAD LIBS
ARE YOU READY
TO MOVE IN TOGETHER?

You've been together for months. You practically live together already,

but is it time to make the _____ move? Take this
ADJECTIVE

_____ quiz to help you decide whether you should start
ADJECTIVE

packing your _____ ... or leave your _____
PLURAL NOUN   PLURAL NOUN

where they are.

Pick which of these _____ scenarios best applies to
ADJECTIVE

you and your _____.
NOUN

(a) You hate being _____, even for _____ seconds.
ADJECTIVE   NUMBER

(b) He drives you out of your _____ when he forgets
PART OF THE BODY

to put down the toilet _____.
NOUN

(c) He always leaves the _____ door open while
NOUN

_____.
VERB ENDING IN "ING"

(d) You discover a stash of _____ in his closet, which
PLURAL NOUN

_____ freaks you out.
ADVERB

Answer: Let's face it, the _____ dollars you'll save on
NUMBER

rent will be worth the _____ gamble on the relationship.
ADJECTIVE

MAD LIBS® is fun to play with friends, but you can also play it by yourself! To begin with, DO NOT look at the story on the page below. Fill in the blanks on this page with the words called for. Then, using the words you have selected, fill in the blank spaces in the story.

Now you've created your own hilarious MAD LIBS® game!

IS HE TOO SELFISH?

VERB _____

ADJECTIVE _____

ADVERB _____

ADJECTIVE _____

ADVERB _____

ADJECTIVE _____

SILLY WORD _____

PART OF THE BODY _____

NUMBER _____

NOUN _____

NOUN _____

ADVERB _____

NUMBER _____

ADJECTIVE _____

PLURAL NOUN _____

PLURAL NOUN _____

NOUN _____

MAD LIBS®

IS HE TOO SELFISH?

Naturally, people have to _____ for themselves, but is
                              VERB

your _____ guy _____ selfish? Take this
         ADJECTIVE   ADVERB

_____ quiz to figure out if he's _____ a good
     ADJECTIVE   ADVERB

guy ... or just a whiny _____ _____ .
                              ADJECTIVE   SILLY WORD

It's your anniversary and he:

(a) Rubs your _____ for _____ minutes
                  PART OF THE BODY   NUMBER

but complains the whole time.

b) Asks if you can postpone your anniversary _____
                                                        NOUN

until tomorrow night. The Super _____ is on tonight.
                                          NOUN

c) _____ makes reservations at your favorite
         ADVERB

restaurant—for you and _____ of his _____ friends.
                            NUMBER   ADJECTIVE

d) Forgets important _____—he's never been very
                          PLURAL NOUN

good about remembering _____ .
                              PLURAL NOUN

Answer: He's a man—of course he's going to be a selfish

_____ .
     NOUN

From TEST YOUR RELATIONSHIP IQ MAD LIBS® • Copyright © 2005 by Chamberlain Bros.,
a division of Penguin Group (USA), Inc., 375 Hudson Street, New York, New York 10014.

MAD LIBS® is fun to play with friends, but you can also play it by yourself! To begin with, DO NOT look at the story on the page below. Fill in the blanks on this page with the words called for. Then, using the words you have selected, fill in the blank spaces in the story.

Now you've created your own hilarious MAD LIBS® game!

ARE YOU TOO DEMANDING?

PLURAL NOUN _____

PLURAL NOUN _____

ADJECTIVE_____

ADJECTIVE_____

ADJECTIVE_____

ROOM _____

VERB _____

NUMBER _____

ADJECTIVE_____

PART OF THE BODY (PLURAL) _____

NOUN _____

NOUN _____

NUMBER _____

ADJECTIVE_____

MAD LIBS®
ARE YOU TOO DEMANDING?

Women certainly know the many _____ to get what
PLURAL NOUN

they want, but are we too demanding of our _____? Take
PLURAL NOUN

this _____ quiz to figure out whether you're just a/an
ADJECTIVE

_____ gal or if you need to learn to a little more flexible.
ADJECTIVE

Which best describes what happens after a/an _____
ADJECTIVE

argument?

(a) You go into the _____, slam the door, and wait for
ROOM

him to _____.
VERB

(b) He spends _____ hours screaming and telling you
NUMBER

that you are _____.
ADJECTIVE

(c) You fall into each other's _____ and you lead
PART OF THE BODY (PLURAL)

him to the _____ immediately.
NOUN

(d) You give him the silent _____ for _____ days
NOUN   NUMBER

before forgiving him.

Answer: Hopefully you picked (c)—you'll get _____
ADJECTIVE

evening out of it!

From TEST YOUR RELATIONSHIP IQ MAD LIBS® • Copyright © 2005 by Chamberlain Bros.,
a division of Penguin Group (USA), Inc., 375 Hudson Street, New York, New York 10014.

MAD LIBS® is fun to play with friends, but you can also play it by yourself! To begin with, DO NOT look at the story on the page below. Fill in the blanks on this page with the words called for. Then, using the words you have selected, fill in the blank spaces in the story.

Now you've created your own hilarious MAD LIBS® game!

IS IT REALLY OVER

PLURAL NOUN _____

NOUN _____

NUMBER _____

EXCLAMATION _____

NOUN _____

PLURAL NOUN _____

A HOLIDAY _____

PLURAL NOUN _____

NOUN _____

NOUN _____

PERSON IN ROOM (FEMALE) _____

MAD LIBS®
IS IT REALLY OVER

You were arguing a lot until he announced it was over. But you're

wondering if it really is. Answer True or False to the following

_____ and find out if there's hope or if you should
_____PLURAL NOUN_____

just get on with your _____.
_____NOUN_____

True or False

1) He'll call you _____ times a day, just to say "_____!"
_____NUMBER_____   _____EXCLAMATION_____

2) He keeps stopping by your _____ to ask for his
_____NOUN_____

_____ back.
_____PLURAL NOUN_____

3) His mother calls you inviting you to _____ _____
_____A HOLIDAY_____PLURAL NOUN

and tells you that he is still thinks the _____ of you.
_____NOUN_____

4) You saw him driving around in a/an _____ that you
_____NOUN_____

think belongs to _____.
_____PERSON IN ROOM (FEMALE)_____

If you answered "True" to number 4, you may as well face it. It's over.

MAD LIBS® is fun to play with friends, but you can also play it by yourself! To begin with, DO NOT look at the story on the page below. Fill in the blanks on this page with the words called for. Then, using the words you have selected, fill in the blank spaces in the story.

Now you've created your own hilarious MAD LIBS® game!

IS HE JUST A JERK?

NOUN _____

NOUN _____

VERB _____

ADJECTIVE_____

ADJECTIVE_____

ADJECTIVE_____

ADJECTIVE_____

ADVERB_____

SILLY WORD_____

VERB _____

VERB _____

EXCLAMATION_____

NOUN _____

ADJECTIVE_____

NOUN _____

NOUN _____

MAD LIBS®
IS HE JUST A JERK?

Sure, he can be an annoying _____ to your friends
NOUN

and sometimes, unexplainably loses his _____, but is he
NOUN

really just a jerk? _____ this quiz to figure out if your
VERB

man is a nice guy or a/an _____ jerk.
ADJECTIVE

His best friend just went through a/an _____
ADJECTIVE

breakup. He responds to the news by saying:

(a) "Are you _____? She was a/an _____!"
ADJECTIVE   ADJECTIVE

(b) "I _____ thought she was a little _____
ADVERB   SILLY WORD

in the head."

(c) "Man, I'm so thrilled I can hardly _____. Now you can
VERB

hang out with me and we can double _____ like old times."
VERB

(d) "_____! She wasn't your _____. She was as
EXCLAMATION   NOUN

_____ as a/an _____ anyway!"
ADJECTIVE   NOUN

Answer: If the answer is (a) and (b), he's a first class jerk, but (c) and

(d) say he's a _____ who cares.
NOUN

From TEST YOUR RELATIONSHIP IQ MAD LIBS® • Copyright © 2005 by Chamberlain Bros.,
a division of Penguin Group (USA), Inc., 375 Hudson Street, New York, New York 10014.

MAD LIBS® is fun to play with friends, but you can also play it by yourself! To begin with, DO NOT look at the story on the page below. Fill in the blanks on this page with the words called for. Then, using the words you have selected, fill in the blank spaces in the story.

Now you've created your own hilarious MAD LIBS® game!

ARE YOU STILL HUNG UP ON HIM?

NUMBER _____

PART OF THE BODY _____

VERB _____

ADJECTIVE _____

OCCUPATION _____

ADJECTIVE _____

ARTICLE OF CLOTHING _____

VERB ENDING IN "ING" _____

NOUN _____

NOUN _____

ADJECTIVE _____

NOUN _____

NOUN _____

NUMBER _____

NOUN _____

NOUN _____

MAD LIBS®
ARE YOU STILL HUNG UP ON HIM?

OK, it's been _____ months since the breakup,
NUMBER

but does your _____ still feel freshly broken?
PART OF THE BODY

_____ this quiz to figure out if you're just feeling
VERB

_____ or are in need of seeing a/an _____.
ADJECTIVE   OCCUPATION

Have you been:

(a) Sleeping in his _____ old _____
ADJECTIVE   ARTICLE OF CLOTHING

every night?

(b) _____ every time you pass the _____
VERB ENDING IN "ING"   NOUN

where you went on your first _____?
NOUN

(c) Setting up a/an _____ shrine to him in your one
ADJECTIVE

room _____?
NOUN

(d) Stopping by his _____ where he works _____
NOUN   NUMBER

times a day to beg him for a second _____?
NOUN

Answer: If you picked (c) or (d), please see a licensed _____
NOUN

immediately.

MAD LIBS® is fun to play with friends, but you can also play it by yourself! To begin with, DO NOT look at the story on the page below. Fill in the blanks on this page with the words called for. Then, using the words you have selected, fill in the blank spaces in the story.

Now you've created your own hilarious MAD LIBS® game!

IS HE ROMANTIC?

PART OF THE BODY _____

ADJECTIVE _____

ADJECTIVE _____

NOUN _____

NOUN _____

ADJECTIVE _____

ADJECTIVE _____

PART OF THE BODY (PLURAL) _____

NOUN _____

ADJECTIVE _____

VERB _____

ADVERB _____

NOUN _____

ADJECTIVE _____

ADJECTIVE _____

ADJECTIVE _____

MAD LIBS

IS HE ROMANTIC?

Sure, he makes your _____ flutter, but does he
PART OF THE BODY

qualify as a/an _____ romantic? Take this _____
ADJECTIVE   ADJECTIVE

quiz to see if he is truly a/an _____ or if he is just like
NOUN

every other _____ you've dated.
NOUN

When you return from a/an _____ business trip and
ADJECTIVE

you're exhausted, does your man . . .

(a) Pick you up at the airport with a/an _____ smile on
ADJECTIVE

his face and a bouquet of roses in his _____.
PART OF THE BODY (PLURAL)

(b) Turn down the volume of the _____ on TV briefly for
NOUN

a/an _____ "hi" when you _____ through the door.
ADJECTIVE   VERB

(c) Act _____ surprised to learn that you've been away.
ADVERB

(d) Expect you to immediately start cooking _____ for him?
NOUN

Answer: (a) makes him a/an _____ romantic at heart.
ADJECTIVE

If you picked (b), (c), or (d), you have a/an _____
ADJECTIVE

apple. The sooner you dump this _____ loser the better.
ADJECTIVE

From TEST YOUR RELATIONSHIP IQ MAD LIBS® • Copyright © 2005 by Chamberlain Bros.,
a division of Penguin Group (USA), Inc., 375 Hudson Street, New York, New York 10014.

MAD LIBS® is fun to play with friends, but you can also play it by yourself! To begin with, DO NOT look at the story on the page below. Fill in the blanks on this page with the words called for. Then, using the words you have selected, fill in the blank spaces in the story.

Now you've created your own hilarious MAD LIBS® game!

IS HE MR. RIGHT?

NOUN _____

ADJECTIVE _____

NOUN _____

ADJECTIVE _____

NOUN _____

NUMBER _____

ADJECTIVE _____

PLURAL NOUN _____

VERB _____

PART OF THE BODY (PLURAL) _____

NOUN _____

ADJECTIVE _____

ADJECTIVE _____

MAD LIBS®
IS HE MR. RIGHT?

He might be the _____ of your life, but you're not sure yet.
                       NOUN

Let this _____ test help you decide if you should go
              ADJECTIVE

shopping for a diamond _____ or stop wasting your
                                NOUN

_____ time.
   ADJECTIVE

Which of the following describes your relationship?

(a) When you call him to make plans, he says "whatever you want,

_____," then argues about it later.
     NOUN

(b) You both want a/an _____-bedroom house in a/an
                              NUMBER

_____ neighborhood in the suburbs and are hoping
     ADJECTIVE

to have children and many _____.
                               PLURAL NOUN

(c) He's noncritical. He adores how you always _____
                                                      VERB

with your _____, which most people find annoying.
             PART OF THE BODY (PLURAL)

(d) Your first name and his last _____ make a/an
                                       NOUN

_____ combination. Right?
   ADJECTIVE

Answer: If you checked (a), you might want to start looking for a/an

_____ guy.
   ADJECTIVE

From TEST YOUR RELATIONSHIP IQ MAD LIBS® • Copyright © 2005 by Chamberlain Bros.,
a division of Penguin Group (USA), Inc., 375 Hudson Street, New York, New York 10014.

MAD LIBS® is fun to play with friends, but you can also play it by yourself! To begin with, DO NOT look at the story on the page below. Fill in the blanks on this page with the words called for. Then, using the words you have selected, fill in the blank spaces in the story.

Now you've created your own hilarious MAD LIBS® game!

IT'S NOT YOU, IT'S ME...

ADJECTIVE_____

PLURAL NOUN _____

ADJECTIVE_____

NOUN _____

EXCLAMATION_____

ADJECTIVE_____

NOUN _____

PLURAL NOUN _____

PLURAL NOUN _____

TYPE OF EVENT _____

VERB (PAST TENSE)_____

VERB ENDING IN "ING" _____

NOUN _____

MAD LIBS

IT'S NOT YOU, IT'S ME . . .

We've all heard it one time or another—the _____
ADJECTIVE

breakup line, "It's not you, it's me." But could it be you? Answer True

or False to the following _____ and find out.
PLURAL NOUN

True or False

1) Whenever he took you to a/an _____ restaurant and
ADJECTIVE

the waiter brought the _____ he would say
NOUN

"_____! You have _____ taste."
EXCLAMATION   ADJECTIVE

2) He says he'll go to your company's _____ party, but
NOUN

when the day arrives, he doesn't show because the _____
PLURAL NOUN

versus the _____ is on ESPN.
PLURAL NOUN

3) He didn't bother to show up at your surprise _____
TYPE OF EVENT

and your whole family was fit to be _____.
VERB (PAST TENSE)

I think I've heard enough. If you answered True to any of these, he's

not _____—it really isn't you, it's _____!
VERB ENDING IN "ING"   NOUN

Now isn't that a relief?

MAD LIBS® is fun to play with friends, but you can also play it by yourself! To begin with, DO NOT look at the story on the page below. Fill in the blanks on this page with the words called for. Then, using the words you have selected, fill in the blank spaces in the story.

Now you've created your own hilarious MAD LIBS® game!

HOW TO RAISE YOUR I.Q.: NUMBER 3

NOUN _____

VERB _____

ADJECTIVE _____

NOUN _____

GEOGRAPHIC LOCATION _____

NOUN _____

GEOGRAPHIC LOCATION _____

GEOGRAPHIC LOCATION _____

PLURAL NOUN _____

NOUN _____

NOUN _____

ADJECTIVE _____

NOUN _____

NOUN _____

VERB ENDING IN "ING" _____

ADJECTIVE _____

You've gone over your Body Language notes, you've been taking

_____ classes and you've even learned how to

NOUN

_____ the Tango, but you're still not in a/an _____

VERB · ADJECTIVE

relationship. Maybe the problem is a little more complex than we

first thought. Here are some ways to deal with the _____:

NOUN

• Go to your local _____. Browse the Self-help section

GEOGRAPHIC LOCATION

for a/an _____ that addresses your particular issue.

NOUN

• Best-sellers like *Men are from* _____, *Women are*

GEOGRAPHIC LOCATION

from _____ have helped numerous people find

GEOGRAPHIC LOCATION

happiness in their _____.

PLURAL NOUN

• Make an appointment with a professional _____.

NOUN

Sometimes there is something in your _____ that is

NOUN

keeping you from finding a/an_____love.

ADJECTIVE

• Call your local _____ and ask if you can meet with

NOUN

an ordained _____. Sometimes just _____

NOUN · VERB ENDING IN "ING"

with a/an _____ person can help.

ADJECTIVE

MAD LIBS® is fun to play with friends, but you can also play it by yourself! To begin with, DO NOT look at the story on the page below. Fill in the blanks on this page with the words called for. Then, using the words you have selected, fill in the blank spaces in the story.

Now you've created your own hilarious MAD LIBS® game!

OFFICE ROMANCE

ADJECTIVE _____

ADJECTIVE _____

NOUN _____

ADJECTIVE _____

ADJECTIVE _____

NOUN _____

PLURAL NOUN _____

VERB ENDING IN "ING" _____

NOUN _____

NOUN _____

MAD LIBS
OFFICE ROMANCE

There is a new guy in the office who you think has real potential.

And he's been acting really _____ around you lately.

ADJECTIVE

Answer True or False to the following questions and find out if

something _____ could come out of this.

ADJECTIVE

True or False

1) He brings you _____ danish every morning just

NOUN

because he knows you like them.

2) He calls you into his office on _____ pretexts and

ADJECTIVE

then will ask you _____ questions about your personal

ADJECTIVE

_____.

NOUN

3) He's invited you out for dinner and _____ after work.

PLURAL NOUN

And he insists on _____ the check!

VERB ENDING IN "ING"

If you answered true to any of these questions why are you taking a

test? You need to pick up the _____, call him into your

NOUN

_____ and conduct some personal business.

NOUN

From TEST YOUR RELATIONSHIP IQ MAD LIBS® • Copyright © 2005 by Chamberlain Bros.,
a division of Penguin Group (USA), Inc., 375 Hudson Street, New York, New York 10014.

MAD LIBS® is fun to play with friends, but you can also play it by yourself! To begin with, DO NOT look at the story on the page below. Fill in the blanks on this page with the words called for. Then, using the words you have selected, fill in the blank spaces in the story.

Now you've created your own hilarious MAD LIBS® game!

SHOULD YOU TAKE HIM BACK?

ADJECTIVE _____

NUMBER _____

ADJECTIVE _____

VERB (PAST TENSE) _____

ADJECTIVE _____

NOUN _____

VERB ENDING IN "ING" _____

TYPE OF FURNITURE _____

VERB ENDING IN "ING" _____

PART OF THE BODY _____

ADJECTIVE _____

ADVERB _____

VERB (PAST TENSE) _____

ADJECTIVE _____

ADJECTIVE _____

TYPE OF FOOD _____

TYPE OF FOOD _____

PART OF THE BODY _____

ADJECTIVE _____

MAD LIBS
SHOULD YOU TAKE
HIM BACK?

You had a/an _____ breakup _____
_____ ADJECTIVE _____ NUMBER

years ago, but now he's back, looking as _____ as ever
_____ ADJECTIVE

and claiming that he has _____ a lot. Take this
_____ VERB (PAST TENSE)

_____ quiz to help you decide whether you should
ADJECTIVE

give him another _____ ... or send him _____.
_____ NOUN _____ VERB ENDING IN "ING"

You're sitting across the _____ from him. What's
_____ TYPE OF FURNITURE

_____ through your mind?
VERB ENDING IN "ING"

(a) Does he still pick his _____?
_____ PART OF THE BODY

(b) All of the _____ fights you used to have, and the
_____ ADJECTIVE

last one where you _____ broke up.
_____ ADVERB

(c) Amazement at how you ever could have _____
_____ VERB (PAST TENSE)

this _____ guy.
_____ ADJECTIVE

(d) The sparks are _____! Should you serve
_____ ADJECTIVE

_____ or _____ at the wedding?
TYPE OF FOOD _____ TYPE OF FOOD

Answer: Let your _____ lead you to the _____
_____ PART OF THE BODY _____ ADJECTIVE

decision.

From TEST YOUR RELATIONSHIP IQ MAD LIBS® • Copyright © 2005 by Chamberlain Bros.,
a division of Penguin Group (USA), Inc., 375 Hudson Street, New York, New York 10014.

Adult
MAD LIBS ®

World's Greatest Word Game

ADVICE FOR THE LOVELORN MAD LIBS

By Roger Price and Leonard Stern

PSS!
PRICE STERN SLOAN

ROADSIDE AMUSEMENTS
an imprint of
CHAMBERLAIN BROS.
Published by the Penguin Group
Price Stern Sloan, a division of Penguin Group for Young Readers.
Penguin Group (USA) Inc., 375 Hudson Street, New York, New York 10014, USA
Penguin Group (Canada), 10 Alcorn Avenue, Toronto, Ontario, Canada M4V 3B2
(a division of Pearson Penguin Canada Inc.)
Penguin Books Ltd, 80 Strand, London WC2R 0RL, England
Penguin Ireland, 25 St Stephen's Green, Dublin 2, Ireland (a division of Penguin Books Ltd)
Penguin Group (Australia), 250 Camberwell Road, Camberwell, Victoria 3124, Australia
(a division of Pearson Australia Group Pty Ltd)
Penguin Books India Pvt Ltd, 11 Community Centre, Panchsheel Park,
New Delhi-110 017, India
Penguin Group (NZ), Cnr Airborne and Rosedale Roads,
Albany, Auckland 1310, New Zealand (a division of Pearson New Zealand Ltd)
Penguin Books (South Africa) (Pty) Ltd, 24 Sturdee Avenue,
Rosebank, Johannesburg 2196, South Africa

Penguin Books Ltd, Registered Offices: 80 Strand, London WC2R 0RL, England

An application has been submitted to register this book with the Library of Congress.

ISBN 1-59609-152-5

Printed in the United States of America

MAD LIBS
INSTRUCTIONS

MAD LIBS® is a game for people who don't like games!
It can be played by one, two, three, four, or forty.

• RIDICULOUSLY SIMPLE DIRECTIONS

In this tablet you will find stories containing blank spaces where words are left out. One player, the **READER**, selects one of these stories. The **READER** does not tell anyone what the story is about. Instead, he/she asks the other players, the **WRITERS**, to give him/her words. These words are used to fill in the blank spaces in the story.

• TO PLAY

The **READER** asks each **WRITER** in turn to call out a word—an adjective or a noun or whatever the space calls for—and uses them to fill in the blank spaces in the story. The result is a **MAD LIBS®** game.

When the **READER** then reads the completed **MAD LIBS®** game to the other players, they will discover that they have written a story that is fantastic, screamingly funny, shocking, silly, crazy, or just plain dumb—depending upon which words each **WRITER** called out.

• EXAMPLE (*Before* and *After*)

"_____!" he said _____
      EXCLAMATION   ADVERB

as he jumped into his convertible _____ and
                                          NOUN

drove off with his _____ wife.
                           ADJECTIVE

"_____*Ouch!*_____!" he said _____*Stupidly*_____
      EXCLAMATION   ADVERB

as he jumped into his convertible _____*Cat*_____ and
                                            NOUN

drove off with his _____*brave*_____ wife.
                         ADJECTIVE

MAD LIBS
QUICK REVIEW

In case you have forgotten what adjectives, adverbs, nouns, and verbs are, here is a quick review:

An **ADJECTIVE** describes something or somebody. *Lumpy, soft, ugly, messy,* and *short* are adjectives.

An **ADVERB** tells how something is done. It modifies a verb and usually ends in "ly." *Modestly, stupidly, greedily,* and *carefully* are adverbs.

A **NOUN** is the name of a person, place, or thing. *Sidewalk, umbrella, bridle, bathtub,* and *nose* are nouns.

A **VERB** is an action word. *Run, pitch, jump,* and *swim* are verbs. Put the verbs in past tense if the directions say PAST TENSE. *Ran, pitched, jumped,* and *swam* are verbs in the past tense.

When we ask for **A PLACE**, we mean any sort of place: a country or city *(Spain, Cleveland)* or a room *(bathroom, kitchen).*

An **EXCLAMATION** or **SILLY WORD** is any sort of funny sound, gasp, grunt, or outcry, like *Wow!, Ouch!, Whomp!, Ick!,* and *Gadzooks!*

When we ask for specific words, like a **NUMBER**, a **COLOR**, an **ANIMAL**, or a **PART OF THE BODY**, we mean a word that is one of those things, like *seven, blue, horse,* or *head.*

When we ask for a **PLURAL**, it means more than one. For example, *cat* pluralized is *cats.*

MAD LIBS® is fun to play with friends, but you can also play it by yourself! To begin with, DO NOT look at the story on the page below. Fill in the blanks on this page with the words called for. Then, using the words you have selected, fill in the blank spaces in the story.

Now you've created your own hilarious MAD LIBS® game!

THE PERFECT BOYFRIEND

NOUN _____

NOUN _____

VERB _____

NUMBER _____

ADJECTIVE_____

ADJECTIVE_____

ADJECTIVE_____

PLURAL NOUN _____

VERB ENDING IN "ING" _____

VERB _____

ADJECTIVE_____

NOUN _____

NOUN _____

NOUN _____

CELEBRITY (MALE)_____

VERB ENDING IN "ING" _____

MAD LIBS
THE PERFECT BOYFRIEND

Let's imagine the perfect boyfriend. He would wake you every

morning with a/an _____. He would use his cell

NOUN

_____ to _____ you _____ times a day.

NOUN ___ VERB ___ NUMBER

He would rub your _____ back after a/an _____

ADJECTIVE ___ ADJECTIVE

day at the _____ office. He would help you shop for

ADJECTIVE

_____ without _____ one bit. He

PLURAL NOUN ___ VERB ENDING IN "ING"

would _____ all of your friends with his _____

VERB ___ ADJECTIVE

charm. He would never click over to a pro _____

NOUN

game while you're watching your favorite episode of

"_____ in the _____." And he wouldn't be

NOUN ___ NOUN

at all jealous of your obsession with _____. Ladies, he is

CELEBRITY (MALE)

out there just _____ for you!

VERB ENDING IN "ING"

From ADVICE FOR THE LOVELORN MAD LIBS® • Copyright © 2005 by Chamberlain Bros.,
a division of Penguin Group (USA), Inc., 375 Hudson Street, New York, New York 10014.

MAD LIBS® is fun to play with friends, but you can also play it by yourself! To begin with, DO NOT look at the story on the page below. Fill in the blanks on this page with the words called for. Then, using the words you have selected, fill in the blank spaces in the story.

Now you've created your own hilarious MAD LIBS® game!

ALL SIGNS POINT TO "BREAK UP"

ADJECTIVE_____

ADVERB_____

ADJECTIVE_____

NOUN _____

PART OF THE BODY _____

ADVERB_____

VERB ENDING IN "ING" _____

NOUN _____

PLURAL NOUN _____

ADJECTIVE_____

ADJECTIVE_____

NUMBER _____

CITY _____

SAME NUMBER_____

SAME CITY_____

ADJECTIVE_____

NUMBER _____

ADVERB_____

ADJECTIVE_____

VERB _____

MAD LIBS®
ALL SIGNS POINT TO
"BREAK UP"

Dear Dating Diva, _____

I have a/an _____ problem. My boyfriend never wants
             ADJECTIVE

to cuddle with me anymore. He's become _____
                                         ADVERB

_____ lately. I've tried having a serious _____
ADJECTIVE   NOUN

discussion with him about this problem, but he just turns his

_____ away and ignores me. The other day, I saw this
PART OF THE BODY

couple _____ in a/an _____ and I almost
      VERB ENDING IN "ING"   NOUN

burst into _____. I love this _____ man
          PLURAL NOUN   ADJECTIVE

and am afraid of becoming a/an _____ spinster if we
                                 ADJECTIVE

break up. What should I do?

—Over _____ in _____
        NUMBER   CITY

Dear _____ in _____,
     SAME NUMBER   SAME CITY

Please reread your _____ letter _____ times. You
                 ADJECTIVE   NUMBER

deserve a man who wants to be with you _____. Get rid
                                     ADVERB

of this _____ jerk and _____ on with your life.
      ADJECTIVE   VERB

From ADVICE FOR THE LOVELORN MAD LIBS® • Copyright © 2005 by Chamberlain Bros.,
a division of Penguin Group (USA), Inc., 375 Hudson Street, New York, New York 10014.

MAD LIBS® is fun to play with friends, but you can also play it by yourself! To begin with, DO NOT look at the story on the page below. Fill in the blanks on this page with the words called for. Then, using the words you have selected, fill in the blank spaces in the story.

Now you've created your own hilarious MAD LIBS® game!

IT'S OVER!

NAME OF PERSON (MALE)_____

NOUN _____

PLURAL NOUN _____

NOUN _____

PLURAL NOUN _____

NOUN _____

PLURAL NOUN _____

NOUN _____

ADJECTIVE_____

TYPE OF FOOD_____

CELEBRITY (MALE)_____

ADJECTIVE_____

ADJECTIVE_____

ADJECTIVE_____

ADVERB_____

MAD LIBS
IT'S OVER!

Dear _____,
     NAME OF PERSON (MALE)

I know this may come as a _____ you, but it's over.
                             NOUN

I've packed my _____ and am going to stay in a friend's
                      PLURAL NOUN

_____ tonight. I just cannot be with a man who spends
  NOUN

several _____ in front of a/an _____ mirror
       PLURAL NOUN   NOUN

every morning, who spends a fortune on _____ and
                              PLURAL NOUN

clothing, and who spends hours waxing his _____. I
                                NOUN

can no longer pretend to be interested in _____ears,
                            ADJECTIVE

cold _____, or _____. Our engagement
      TYPE OF FOOD   CELEBRITY (MALE)

is off. I hope you find someone else as _____ as you
                         ADJECTIVE

so that you can both be _____ together.
                  ADJECTIVE

_____,
  ADVERB

Me

From ADVICE FOR THE LOVELORN MAD LIBS® • Copyright © 2005 by Chamberlain Bros.,
a division of Penguin Group (USA), Inc., 375 Hudson Street, New York, New York 10014.

MAD LIBS® is fun to play with friends, but you can also play it by yourself! To begin with, DO NOT look at the story on the page below. Fill in the blanks on this page with the words called for. Then, using the words you have selected, fill in the blank spaces in the story.

Now you've created your own hilarious MAD LIBS® game!

INDULGE YOURSELF

ADJECTIVE _____

ADJECTIVE _____

ADJECTIVE _____

TYPE OF CONTAINER _____

PLURAL NOUN _____

PLURAL NOUN _____

NOUN _____

ADVERB _____

PLURAL NOUN _____

NUMBER _____

PART OF THE BODY _____

ADJECTIVE _____

VERB _____

VERB _____

PLURAL NOUN _____

VERB _____

ADJECTIVE _____

ICE CREAM

MAD LIBS®
INDULGE YOURSELF

Don't even try to stay on your _____ diet after a/an
ADJECTIVE

_____ breakup! You now have a really _____
ADJECTIVE   ADJECTIVE

excuse to eat a/an _____ full of chopped
                        TYPE OF CONTAINER

_____ and as many chocolate _____ as
PLURAL NOUN   PLURAL NOUN

your _____ desires. What else would go so _____
        NOUN   ADVERB

with your viewings of "Desperate _____ _____"?
                                        ADJECTIVE   PLURAL NOUN

Who cares if those _____ calories go straight to your
                        NUMBER

_____? You're going through a very _____
PART OF THE BODY   ADJECTIVE

time. Plus, you can just _____ to the gym tomorrow
                              VERB

and _____ an extra 30 _____ minutes.
        VERB   PLURAL NOUN

Who knows, you might _____ the eye of your
                          VERB

_____ soul mate as you _____ on the
ADJECTIVE   VERB

StairMaster.

MAD LIBS® is fun to play with friends, but you can also play it by yourself! To begin with, DO NOT look at the story on the page below. Fill in the blanks on this page with the words called for. Then, using the words you have selected, fill in the blank spaces in the story.

Now you've created your own hilarious MAD LIBS® game!

POST-BREAKUP PURGING

VERB ENDING IN "ING" _____

ADJECTIVE _____

ADJECTIVE _____

CITY _____

ADJECTIVE _____

NUMBER _____

VERB _____

ADJECTIVE _____

ARTICLE OF CLOTHING _____

ADJECTIVE _____

ADJECTIVE _____

NOUN _____

TYPE OF LIQUID _____

ADJECTIVE _____

A PLACE _____

VERB _____

TYPE OF CONTAINER _____

EXCLAMATION _____

VERB ENDING IN "ING" _____

NOUN _____

MAD LIBS®
POST-BREAKUP PURGING

Are you still _____ over those _____
  VERB ENDING IN "ING"   _ADJECTIVE_

photos from your _____ trip to _____
                        ADJECTIVE   _CITY_

harbor? Have you read and reread the _____ notes he
                                              ADJECTIVE

wrote to you _____ times? Do you still _____
                  NUMBER   _VERB_

in his _____ _____? It's time to get
          ADJECTIVE   _ARTICLE OF CLOTHING_

over that _____ feeling by tossing all evidence of your
              ADJECTIVE

_____ relationship into a big fire (just make sure you
  ADJECTIVE

have some _____ nearby in case the flames become
              TYPE OF LIQUID

too _____). You could also bury everything in the
        ADJECTIVE

_____. Or you can just _____ it in the
  A PLACE   _VERB_

_____. _____! You're well on the way
  TYPE OF CONTAINER   _EXCLAMATION_

to _____ him out of your _____!
      VERB ENDING IN "ING"   _NOUN_

From ADVICE FOR THE LOVELORN MAD LIBS® • Copyright © 2005 by Chamberlain Bros., a division of Penguin Group (USA), Inc., 375 Hudson Street, New York, New York 10014.

MAD LIBS® is fun to play with friends, but you can also play it by yourself! To begin with, DO NOT look at the story on the page below. Fill in the blanks on this page with the words called for. Then, using the words you have selected, fill in the blank spaces in the story.

Now you've created your own hilarious MAD LIBS® game!

CLASSIC LOVE LETTER

ADJECTIVE _____

ADJECTIVE _____

VERB _____

NOUN _____

VERB ENDING IN "ING" _____

NOUN _____

VERB _____

PART OF THE BODY (PLURAL) _____

VERB _____

NOUN _____

ADJECTIVE _____

ADJECTIVE _____

PART OF THE BODY _____

NOUN _____

MAD LIBS®
CLASSIC LOVE LETTER

Before you start thinking that _____ love doesn't exist,
                                  ADJECTIVE

check out this love _____ letter that Irish writer James
                      ADJECTIVE

Joyce wrote to his wife, Nora:

My own _____ Nora,
          ADJECTIVE

I love you, I cannot _____ without you. . . . I would
                      VERB

like to go through _____ side by side with you,
                    NOUN

_____ you more and more until we grew to be one
VERB ENDING IN "ING"

_____ together until the hour should come for us
      NOUN

to _____ .
    VERB

Even now the tears rush to my _____ and sobs
                           PART OF THE BODY (PLURAL)

_____ my throat as I write this. . . .
    VERB

O my _____ be only a little kinder to me, bear with
       NOUN

me a little even if I am _____ and _____
                  ADJECTIVE   ADJECTIVE

and believe me we will be happy together.

Let me have your _____ always close to mine to hear
             PART OF THE BODY

every throb of my life, every _____, every joy. —James Joyce
                  NOUN

MAD LIBS® is fun to play with friends, but you can also play it by yourself! To begin with, DO NOT look at the story on the page below. Fill in the blanks on this page with the words called for. Then, using the words you have selected, fill in the blank spaces in the story.

Now you've created your own hilarious MAD LIBS® game!

DROWN YOUR SORROWS

ADJECTIVE _Ugly_

VERB _Drinking_

ADJECTIVE _Grundgy_

ADJECTIVE _Trashy_

PART OF THE BODY _Finger_

NOUN _Stool_

NOUN _Fools_

TYPE OF PLANT _Pot_

TYPE OF ALCOHOL _Beer_

TYPE OF LIQUID _Beer_

ADJECTIVE _Whorish_

TYPE OF FRUIT _Mellon_

TYPE OF VEGETABLE _Zuccini_

CELEBRITY DIVA _Mariah_

TYPE OF LIQUID _Beer_

ADJECTIVE _Sluty_

MAD LIBS®
DROWN YOUR SORROWS

Fresh from a/an _____ relationship, you deserve a
                     ADJECTIVE

drink. What better time is there to _____ your libation
                                          VERB

horizons and pick a/an _____ signature "chicktail" to
                              ADJECTIVE

celebrate your freedom? To satisfy your _____ tooth,
                                                ADJECTIVE

order a Fuzzy _____, a concoction of _____
              PART OF THE BODY   NOUN

juice and _____liquor. Or there's the Mojito, made
            NOUN

with _____, _____, and a splash of
      TYPE OF PLANT   ANOTHER TYPE OF ALCOHOL

_____. If you're in a retro mood, Martinis now come
  TYPE OF LIQUID

in all sorts of _____ varieties. Try a/an _____-tini
                  ADJECTIVE   TYPE OF FRUIT

or a/an _____-tini. Or maybe a _____,
          TYPE OF VEGETABLE   CELEBRITY DIVA

libation made with gin and a spritz of _____.
                                              TYPE OF LIQUID

Experiment until you find your most _____ new favorite!
                                         ADJECTIVE

From MAD LIBS® ADVICE FOR THE LOVELORN • Copyright © 2005 by Chamberlain Bros.,
a division of Penguin Group (USA), Inc., New York, 375 Hudson Street, New York, New York 10014.

MAD LIBS® is fun to play with friends, but you can also play it by yourself! To begin with, DO NOT look at the story on the page below. Fill in the blanks on this page with the words called for. Then, using the words you have selected, fill in the blank spaces in the story.

Now you've created your own hilarious MAD LIBS® game!

GIRLS' NIGHT OUT

VERB _____

ANIMAL (PLURAL) _____

ADJECTIVE_____

ADJECTIVE_____

ADJECTIVE_____

NOUN _____

VERB _____

ADJECTIVE_____

PART OF THE BODY _____

ADJECTIVE_____

PLURAL NOUN _____

NOUN _____

NOUN _____

Sometimes you just want to _____ with your
VERB

girlfriends without having to fend off _____ all
ANIMAL (PLURAL)

night—particularly after going through a/an _____
ADJECTIVE

breakup. You're just not up to creating _____ responses
ADJECTIVE

to _____ one-liners. Well, the truth is that most
ADJECTIVE

men are intimidated by women, and if you give off the right

_____, they'll _____ away from you.
NOUN   VERB

Follow these tips to enjoy your _____ girls' night out
ADJECTIVE

uninterrupted:

- Don't make lingering _____ contact.
  PART OF THE BODY

- Opt out of the _____ contests.
  ADJECTIVE

- Don't allow the _____ to dance too close.
  PLURAL NOUN

- Resist the urge to dance on top of the _____.
  NOUN

- Keep yourself from yelling, "Who's going to buy me a/an

  _____!"
  NOUN

MAD LIBS® is fun to play with friends, but you can also play it by yourself! To begin with, DO NOT look at the story on the page below. Fill in the blanks on this page with the words called for. Then, using the words you have selected, fill in the blank spaces in the story.

Now you've created your own hilarious MAD LIBS® game!

A DOUBLE WHAMMY

ADJECTIVE _____

NUMBER _____

ADJECTIVE _____

PLURAL NOUN _____

PART OF THE BODY _____

ADVERB _____

ADJECTIVE _____

ARTICLE OF CLOTHING _____

ADVERB _____

SILLY WORD _____

SAME SILLY WORD _____

ADJECTIVE _____

ADJECTIVE _____

ANIMAL _____

VERB _____

PLURAL NOUN _____

VERB _____

ADJECTIVE _____

MAD LIBS

A DOUBLE WHAMMY

Dear Dating Diva,

I am such a/an _____ loser. My boyfriend of _____
        ADJECTIVE   NUMBER

months just left me for my _____ friend. I guess the
                                    ADJECTIVE

obvious _____ were all there: prolonged _____
            PLURAL NOUN   PART OF THE BODY

contact, the fact that he _____ invited her along on
                                ADVERB

our_____ dates, and then there's the time I found her
        ADJECTIVE

_____ in his _____. Still, I'm feeling
ARTICLE OF CLOTHING   NOUN

_____ betrayed. How will I ever get over this?
        ADVERB

— _____
        SILLY WORD

Dear _____,
        SAME SILLY WORD

Of course you're feeling _____, but you're better off,
                                ADJECTIVE

Believe me! She was not a very _____ friend. And he's
                                        ADJECTIVE

just proven himself to be a pretty stupid _____.
                                                    ANIMAL

_____ for a couple of days and then, for _____
        VERB   PLURAL NOUN

sake _____ on with your _____ life.
            VERB   ADJECTIVE

From ADVICE FOR THE LOVELORN MAD LIBS® • Copyright © 2005 by Chamberlain Bros.,
a division of Penguin Group (USA), Inc., 375 Hudson Street, New York, New York 10014.

MAD LIBS® is fun to play with friends, but you can also play it by yourself! To begin with, DO NOT look at the story on the page below. Fill in the blanks on this page with the words called for. Then, using the words you have selected, fill in the blank spaces in the story.

Now you've created your own hilarious MAD LIBS® game!

MAKEOVER

NUMBER _____

VERB _____

PLURAL NOUN _____

ADJECTIVE _____

ADJECTIVE _____

PLURAL NOUN _____

CITY _____

CELEBRITY (FEMALE) _____

NOUN _____

VERB ENDING IN "ING" _____

ADJECTIVE _____

COLOR _____

COLOR _____

NOUN _____

ADJECTIVE _____

ADVERB _____

ADJECTIVE _____

ADVERB _____

ADJECTIVE _____

MAD LIBS
MAKEOVER

It's been _____ months since the break-up and it's time
         NUMBER

to _____ out there again. How about a makeover to
      VERB

show your _____ you're not the same _____
            PLURAL NOUN   ADJECTIVE

girl anymore? First, remember that when it comes to cosmetics, less is

_____. "Too much makeup adds _____,
      ADJECTIVE   PLURAL NOUN

makes you look older," according to one _____ make-up
                                             CITY

artist, who works with _____. Instead of reaching for
                         CELEBRITY (FEMALE)

the _____ of years past, try _____
         NOUN   VERB ENDING IN "ING"

products, which can brighten your _____ skin. The
                                      ADJECTIVE

_____ and _____ hues can be mixed
      COLOR   COLOR

with your favorite _____ and applied to your skin to
                       NOUN

ensure the _____ look you desire. But proceed
                ADJECTIVE

_____ because glittery makeup looks best on younger
      ADVERB

_____. Not that you're old but well, you're older than
   PLURAL NOUN

before he dumped you, and time stops for no _____.
                                                  NOUN

Sorry!

From ADVICE FOR THE LOVELORN MAD LIBS® • Copyright © 2005 by Chamberlain Bros.,
a division of Penguin Group (USA), Inc., 375 Hudson Street, New York, New York 10014.

MAD LIBS® is fun to play with friends, but you can also play it by yourself! To begin with, DO NOT look at the story on the page below. Fill in the blanks on this page with the words called for. Then, using the words you have selected, fill in the blank spaces in the story.

Now you've created your own hilarious MAD LIBS® game!

LET US COUNT THE WAYS

ANIMAL _____

VERB ENDING IN "ING" _____

ADJECTIVE _____

ADJECTIVE _____

VERB _____

PLURAL NOUN _____

ADJECTIVE _____

PLURAL NOUN _____

ADJECTIVE _____

CELEBRITY (FEMALE) _____

NOUN _____

PART OF THE BODY _____

ADJECTIVE _____

EXCLAMATION _____

ADVERB _____

ADJECTIVE _____

ADJECTIVE _____

MAD LIBS

LET US COUNT THE WAYS

That guy was real _____. Instead of _____
ANIMAL   VERB ENDING IN "ING"

around, reminiscing about all the _____ times you
ADJECTIVE

had together, think of some of the _____ reasons you
ADJECTIVE

don't want to _____ him, anymore.
VERB

• He never sent you a dozen _____ on your birthday.
PLURAL NOUN

• His idea of a/an _____ evening was buying frozen
ADJECTIVE

_____ at a/an _____ market.
PLURAL NOUN   ADJECTIVE

• He was obsessed with _____, and you know she
CELEBRITY (FEMALE)

wouldn't give him the time of _____.
NOUN

• His _____ was pretty _____.
PART OF THE BODY   ADJECTIVE

• His greeting was always "_____!"
EXCLAMATION

• He didn't realize what a/an _____ _____
ADVERB   ADJECTIVE

gal he had!

• He is a/an _____ loser.
ADJECTIVE

MAD LIBS® is fun to play with friends, but you can also play it by yourself! To begin with, DO NOT look at the story on the page below. Fill in the blanks on this page with the words called for. Then, using the words you have selected, fill in the blank spaces in the story.

Now you've created your own hilarious MAD LIBS® game!

DANCE THERAPY

ADJECTIVE_____

NOUN _____

NOUN _____

ADVERB_____

VERB _____

ADJECTIVE_____

NOUN _____

ADJECTIVE_____

NUMBER (PLURAL) _____

PART OF THE BODY (PLURAL) _____

ADJECTIVE_____

VERB _____

VERB _____

PART OF THE BODY _____

ADJECTIVE_____

PLURAL NOUN _____

ADJECTIVE_____

PLURAL NOUN _____

MAD LIBS

DANCE THERAPY

Sometimes the cure for a/an _____ heart is to dance
ADJECTIVE

until the wee hours of the _____ with your girlfriends
NOUN

at a/an _____ club. Now that you're _____
NOUN   ADVERB

on the market, you'll need to _____ up on your dance
VERB

moves. Here are some _____ tips for boogying down—
ADJECTIVE

in your own _____ or in front of a/an _____
A PLACE   ADJECTIVE

crowd of _____:
PLURAL NOUN

• Rotate your _____ to the music, of course.
PART OF THE BODY (PLURAL)

• If you have _____ hair, _____ it with
ADJECTIVE   VERB

all you've got—but don't get so dizzy that you _____.
VERB

• Be sure to move your _____ with purpose—flailing
PART OF THE BODY

is not attractive or _____.
ADJECTIVE

• Put your hands on your _____ to look ultra-_____.
PLURAL NOUN   ADJECTIVE

In no time at all, you'll be attracting many _____.
PLURAL NOUN

From ADVICE FOR THE LOVELORN MAD LIBS® • Copyright © 2005 by Chamberlain Bros.,
a division of Penguin Group (USA), Inc., 375 Hudson Street, New York, New York 10014.

MAD LIBS® is fun to play with friends, but you can also play it by yourself! To begin with, DO NOT look at the story on the page below. Fill in the blanks on this page with the words called for. Then, using the words you have selected, fill in the blank spaces in the story.

Now you've created your own hilarious MAD LIBS® game!

EVEN CELEBRITIES GET DUMPED

CELEBRITY (MALE) _____

NOUN _____

CITY _____

VERB _____

ADJECTIVE _____

NOUN _____

NOUN _____

VERB ENDING IN "ING" _____

CELEBRITY (FEMALE) _____

ADJECTIVE _____

ADVERB _____

NOUN _____

EXCLAMATION _____

ADVERB _____

CELEBRITY (FEMALE) _____

VERB ENDING IN "ING" _____

ADJECTIVE _____

MAD LIBS
EVEN CELEBRITIES GET DUMPED

Dear _____,
<u>CELEBRITY (MALE)</u>

By the time you read this, I will be on my private _____ flying
<u>NOUN</u>

to _____ to _____ my new album. You
<u>CITY</u>   <u>VERB</u>

_____ piece of _____! Check out page
<u>ADJECTIVE</u>   <u>NOUN</u>

three in the new issue of _____ magazine. There you are,
<u>NOUN</u>

_____ with _____ at a/an _____
<u>VERB ENDING IN "ING"</u>   <u>CELEBRITY (FEMALE)</u>   <u>ADJECTIVE</u>

party! I knew you had fallen _____ in love with her
<u>ADVERB</u>

when I saw you do that passionate _____ scene last
<u>NOUN</u>

month. _____, we're through!
<u>EXCLAMATION</u>

_____,
<u>ADVERB</u>

_____
<u>CELEBRITY (FEMALE)</u>

PS—And don't even think of _____ up at my
<u>VERB ENDING IN "ING"</u>

_____ premiere next month!
<u>ADJECTIVE</u>

MAD LIBS® is fun to play with friends, but you can also play it by yourself! To begin with, DO NOT look at the story on the page below. Fill in the blanks on this page with the words called for. Then, using the words you have selected, fill in the blank spaces in the story.

Now you've created your own hilarious MAD LIBS® game!

A LITTLE CHEERING UP

ADJECTIVE _hairy_

PART OF THE BODY _penis_

ADVERB _forcefully_

ANIMAL _tiger_

EXCLAMATION _grunt_

ADJECTIVE _tall_

ADJECTIVE _lumpy_

NOUN _forest_

VERB _smack_

PLURAL NOUN _dildos_

ADVERB _carefully_

OCCUPATION _taxi driver_

ADJECTIVE _wet_

NOUN _park_

NUMBER _35_

VERB _kick_

MAD LIBS®
A LITTLE CHEERING UP

It's natural for you to be feeling a little _____ so soon
ADJECTIVE

after having your _____ broken so _____
PART OF THE BODY   ADVERB

by that clueless _____. _____! Now is
ANIMAL   EXCLAMATION

not the time for you to forget how _____ you are. Let
ADJECTIVE

us remind you:

• You are so _____ that a/an _____
ADJECTIVE   NOUN

should be named after you!

• Men _____ all over their _____ when
VERB   PLURAL NOUN

you walk by!

• You are so _____ intelligent that you could easily be a
ADVERB

successful _____!
OCCUPATION

• Your wit is so _____ you could make a/an _____
ADJECTIVE   NOUN

double over with laughter!

• There are _____ guys out there who would _____
NUMBER   VERB

to be by your side!

MAD LIBS® is fun to play with friends, but you can also play it by yourself! To begin with, DO NOT look at the story on the page below. Fill in the blanks on this page with the words called for. Then, using the words you have selected, fill in the blank spaces in the story.

Now you've created your own hilarious MAD LIBS® game!

ANOTHER TRY?

ADVERB _____

ADJECTIVE _____

PLURAL NOUN _____

ADVERB _____

VERB _____

ANIMAL _____

VERB _____

ADJECTIVE _____

PLURAL NOUN _____

PART OF THE BODY _____

NOUN _____

MAD LIBS®
ANOTHER TRY?

You're so _____ wonderful that it's bound to happen:
         ADVERB

A knock on your front door, and there he is, with his _____
                                                    ADJECTIVE

eyes and an armful of _____. He tells you he misses
                        PLURAL NOUN

you _____; he can't _____ without you. He
      ADVERB   VERB

realizes he's made a complete _____ of himself and
                                  ANIMAL

wants to _____ back together. Do you love him still?
           VERB

Only you know the _____ answer, but just remember that
                    ADJECTIVE

only five _____ ago he _____ out on you
           PLURAL NOUN   VERB (PAST TENSE)

and broke your _____. Be sure you know whether
                PART OF THE BODY

he really wants to get back together or if he's just looking for a place

to hang his _____.
              NOUN

MAD LIBS® is fun to play with friends, but you can also play it by yourself! To begin with, DO NOT look at the story on the page below. Fill in the blanks on this page with the words called for. Then, using the words you have selected, fill in the blank spaces in the story.

Now you've created your own hilarious MAD LIBS® game!

BACK IN THE SADDLE

ADVERB _____

ADJECTIVE _____

NOUN _____

VERB _____

ADJECTIVE _____

PART OF THE BODY _____

TYPE OF FOOD _____

VERB ENDING IN "ING" _____

ADJECTIVE _____

NOUN _____

NOUN _____

NOUN _____

NOUN _____

VERB _____

ADJECTIVE _____

ADJECTIVE _____

NOUN _____

VERB ENDING IN "ING" _____

MAD LIBS®
BACK IN THE SADDLE

Sure, you've just been _____ burned by that

ADVERB

_____ _____, but you just can't

ADJECTIVE   NOUN

_____ around. You're not going to waste the most

VERB

_____ years of your life by stuffing your _____

ADJECTIVE   PART OF THE BODY

with _____ and _____ on your sofa every

TYPE OF FOOD   VERB ENDING IN "ING"

night. Here are some really _____ tips to get you back

ADJECTIVE

into the real _____:

NOUN

• Volunteer at your neighborhood _____

NOUN

• Join a locoal sports _____

NOUN

• Adopt a pet _____

NOUN

• _____ up a/an _____ new hobby

VERB   ADJECTIVE

• Travel to a/an _____ far off _____

ADJECTIVE   NOUN

• Go _____with your girlfriends

VERB ENDING IN "ING"

MAD LIBS® is fun to play with friends, but you can also play it by yourself! To begin with, DO NOT look at the story on the page below. Fill in the blanks on this page with the words called for. Then, using the words you have selected, fill in the blank spaces in the story.

Now you've created your own hilarious MAD LIBS® game!

KNOW YOUR TYPE
PART ONE

NOUN _____

ADJECTIVE _____

NOUN _____

ADJECTIVE _____

VERB _____

ADJECTIVE _____

PLURAL NOUN _____

ADJECTIVE _____

NOUN _____

PLURAL NOUN _____

NOUN _____

ADJECTIVE _____

VERB _____

ADJECTIVE _____

ADJECTIVE _____

MAD LIBS
KNOW YOUR TYPE
PART ONE

Chances are you've known a few losers in your day. Here's a/an

guide to help you decide who gets your _____ and who
                                           NOUN

_____ gets shown to the _____.
   ADJECTIVE   NOUN

• Artist: When this guy writes a/an _____ poem about
                                         ADJECTIVE

you or paints a flattering portrait of you, you'll _____ faster
                                                        VERB

than ice cream on a/an _____ day. Warning: avoid
                            ADJECTIVE

"tortured" artists who still live with their _____.
                                                 PLURAL NOUN

• Professional: This guy will overwhelm you with his _____
                                                          ADJECTIVE

dedication to his _____—not to mention his well-
                       NOUN

tailored _____. Warning: He can spend too many
              PLURAL NOUN

hours at a/an place instead of at your gorgeous side.

• Hipster: Very trendy, this guy will take you to the most

_____ spots in town where you'll _____
   ADJECTIVE   VERB

about the '80s. Warning: will probably have a/an _____
                                                      ADJECTIVE

ego and a/an _____ wardrobe that puts yours to shame.
                 ADJECTIVE

From ADVICE FOR THE LOVELORN MAD LIBS® • Copyright © 2005 by Chamberlain Bros.,
a division of Penguin Group (USA), Inc., 375 Hudson Street, New York, New York 10014.

MAD LIBS® is fun to play with friends, but you can also play it by yourself! To begin with, DO NOT look at the story on the page below. Fill in the blanks on this page with the words called for. Then, using the words you have selected, fill in the blank spaces in the story.

Now you've created your own hilarious MAD LIBS® game!

WWW.INTERNETDATINGADVERTISEMENT.COM

ADJECTIVE _____

NOUN _____

NOUN _____

ADJECTIVE _____

ADJECTIVE _____

ADJECTIVE _____

NOUN _____

ADJECTIVE _____

NOUN _____

NOUN _____

PLURAL NOUN _____

PLURAL NOUN _____

PLURAL NOUN _____

ADJECTIVE _____

NOUN _____

Tired of meeting _____ men in bars, _____
                       ADJECTIVE   NOUN

parties or the _____ store? You're not alone. That's
                                 NOUN

why today, many _____ women are using the Internet to find
                          ADJECTIVE

their _____ man. We at www.golden_____.com
     ADJECTIVE   NOUN

will use our _____-tested, system for matching you
                        NOUN

with the _____ of your dreams based on your shared
                    NOUN

values regarding _____ , _____, and
                    PLURAL NOUN   PLURAL NOUN

_____. Our method is so _____ that
     PLURAL NOUN   ADJECTIVE

we guarantee you'll have a/an _____ on your finger in
                                     NOUN

no time!

MAD LIBS® is fun to play with friends, but you can also play it by yourself! To begin with, DO NOT look at the story on the page below. Fill in the blanks on this page with the words called for. Then, using the words you have selected, fill in the blank spaces in the story.

Now you've created your own hilarious MAD LIBS® game!

KNOW YOUR TYPE
PART TWO

VERB _____

NOUN _____

VERB ENDING IN "ING" _____

PART OF THE BODY (PLURAL) _____

ADJECTIVE_____

CELEBRITY (FEMALE) _____

NOUN _____

NOUN _____

ADJECTIVE_____

VERB ENDING IN "ING" _____

NOUN _____

PART OF THE BODY (PLURAL) _____

ADJECTIVE_____

ANIMAL _____

VERB ENDING IN "ING" _____

ADJECTIVE_____

PLURAL NOUN _____

ADJECTIVE_____

MAD LIBS®
KNOW YOUR TYPE
PART TWO

• Athlete: Whether you _____ this guy at the gym, a
                              VERB

sports _____, or _____ in the park,
              NOUN   VERB ENDING IN "ING"

you'll be impressed by his killer _____. Warning:
                                      PART OF THE BODY (PLURAL)

if in time you discover a/an _____ poster of
                                    ADJECTIVE

_____ hanging over his _____ don't be surprised.
CELEBRITY (FEMALE)   NOUN

• Environmentalist: This guy will woo you with his

_____ and a really _____ commitment to
        NOUN   ADJECTIVE

_____ the planet. He will certainly be happy if you
VERB ENDING IN "ING"

don't wear a/an fur _____ or don't shave your
                          NOUN

_____. Warning: may be in need of a long,
PART OF THE BODY (PLURAL)

_____ shower.
     ADJECTIVE

• Geek: Having been the under-_____ for so long, this
                                      ANIMAL

guy is usually very _____ and sensitive. He probably
                        VERB ENDING IN "ING"

spent his adolescence _____, so he is probably
                              VERB ENDING IN "ING"

_____ and successful. Warning: may not have many
        ADJECTIVE

_____ and may be in need of a/an _____ makeover.
PLURAL NOUN   ADJECTIVE

From ADVICE FOR THE LOVELORN MAD LIBS® • Copyright © 2005 by Chamberlain Bros.,
a division of Penguin Group (USA), Inc., 375 Hudson Street, New York, New York 10014.

MAD LIBS® is fun to play with friends, but you can also play it by yourself! To begin with, DO NOT look at the story on the page below. Fill in the blanks on this page with the words called for. Then, using the words you have selected, fill in the blank spaces in the story.

Now you've created your own hilarious MAD LIBS® game!

BEWARE THE FREAKS!

ADJECTIVE_____

ADJECTIVE_____

VERB ENDING IN "ING" _____

PART OF THE BODY (PLURAL) _____

VERB _____

ADJECTIVE_____

NOUN _____

ADVERB_____

ADVERB_____

SAME ADVERB _____

NOUN _____

ADJECTIVE_____

MAD LIBS®

BEWARE THE FREAKS!

Dear Dating Diva,

I really need some _____ advice. This _____
         ADJECTIVE   ADJECTIVE

guy and I were _____ last week when I discovered
           VERB ENDING IN "ING"

he has three _____! At first I thought I could
          PART OF THE BODY (PLURAL)

_____ with it, but now I just think it's really _____.
     VERB   ADJECTIVE

He's called me several times since the incident, asking me out on

another _____. I'm _____ lonely.
            NOUN   ADVERB

Should I try to get over this?

_____ Confused .
     ADVERB

Dear _____ Confused,
        SAME ADVERB

You should see a professional _____ about this
                                      NOUN

_____ problem.
    ADJECTIVE

MAD LIBS® is fun to play with friends, but you can also play it by yourself! To begin with, DO NOT look at the story on the page below. Fill in the blanks on this page with the words called for. Then, using the words you have selected, fill in the blank spaces in the story.

Now you've created your own hilarious MAD LIBS® game!

WHAT TO DO?

ADJECTIVE_____

NUMBER _____

ADJECTIVE_____

VERB ENDING IN "ING" _____

NOUN _____

NUMBER _____

ADJECTIVE_____

VERB _____

ADJECTIVE_____

PLURAL NOUN _____

ADJECTIVE_____

VERB _____

ADJECTIVE_____

CITY _____

SAME ADJECTIVE _____

SAME CITY_____

VERB _____

MAD LIBS®
WHAT TO DO?

Dear Dating Diva,

Help! I've been seeing this _____ guy for
ADJECTIVE

_____ weeks, and everything was _____
NUMBER   ADJECTIVE

until last week. We were talking about _____ on
VERB ENDING IN "ING"

a/an _____ together, when he told me he's seeing
NOUN

_____ other women, some of whom are quite _____!
NUMBER   ADJECTIVE

I really want to _____ this guy—he's really very
VERB

_____ and buys me lots of _____.
ADJECTIVE   PLURAL NOUN

I'm just not sure I can get past his _____ confession.
ADJECTIVE

How should I _____ this?
VERB

— _____ in _____
ADJECTIVE   CITY

Dear _____ in _____,
SAME ADJECTIVE   SAME CITY

Three words: _____ him, immediately!
VERB

Adult

MAD LIBS®

World's Greatest Word Game

KEEPERS AND LOSERS MAD LIBS

By Roger Price and Leonard Stern

PSS!
PRICE STERN SLOAN

ROADSIDE AMUSEMENTS
an imprint of
CHAMBERLAIN BROS.
Price Stern Sloan, a division of Penguin Group for Young Readers.
Published by the Penguin Group
Penguin Group (USA) Inc., 375 Hudson Street, New York, New York 10014, USA
Penguin Group (Canada), 10 Alcorn Avenue, Toronto, Ontario, Canada M4V 3B2
(a division of Pearson Penguin Canada Inc.)
Penguin Books Ltd, 80 Strand, London WC2R 0RL, England
Penguin Ireland, 25 St Stephen's Green, Dublin 2, Ireland (a division of Penguin Books Ltd)
Penguin Group (Australia), 250 Camberwell Road, Camberwell, Victoria 3124, Australia
(a division of Pearson Australia Group Pty Ltd)
Penguin Books India Pvt Ltd, 11 Community Centre, Panchsheel Park,
New Delhi-110 017, India
Penguin Group (NZ), Cnr Airborne and Rosedale Roads,
Albany, Auckland 1310, New Zealand (a division of Pearson New Zealand Ltd)
Penguin Books (South Africa) (Pty) Ltd, 24 Sturdee Avenue,
Rosebank, Johannesburg 2196, South Africa

Penguin Books Ltd, Registered Offices: 80 Strand, London WC2R 0RL, England

An application has been submitted to register this book with the Library of Congress.

ISBN 1-59609-150-9

Printed in the United States of America

PSS! and MAD LIBS are a registered trademark of Penguin Group (USA) Inc.

MAD LIBS

INSTRUCTIONS

MAD LIBS® is a game for people who don't like games!
It can be played by one, two, three, four, or forty.

• RIDICULOUSLY SIMPLE DIRECTIONS

In this tablet you will find stories containing blank spaces where words are
left out. One player, the READER, selects one of these stories. The READER
does not tell anyone what the story is about. Instead, he/she asks the other
players, the WRITERS, to give him/her words. These words are used to fill in
the blank spaces in the story.

• TO PLAY

The READER asks each WRITER in turn to call out a word—an adjective or
a noun or whatever the space calls for—and uses them to fill in the blank
spaces in the story. The result is a MAD LIBS® game.

When the READER then reads the completed MAD LIBS® game to the
other players, they will discover that they have written a story that is
fantastic, screamingly funny, shocking, silly, crazy, or just plain dumb—
depending upon which words each WRITER called out.

• EXAMPLE (Before and After)

" _____ !" he said _____
          EXCLAMATION   ADVERB

as he jumped into his convertible _____ and
                                               NOUN

drove off with his _____ wife.
                          ADJECTIVE

" _____*Ouch*_____ !" he said _____*Stupidly*_____
          EXCLAMATION   ADVERB

as he jumped into his convertible _____*cat*_____ and
                                               NOUN

drove off with his _____*brave*_____ wife.
                          ADJECTIVE

MAD LIBS®
QUICK REVIEW

In case you have forgotten what adjectives, adverbs, nouns, and verbs are, here is a quick review:

An **ADJECTIVE** describes something or somebody. *Lumpy, soft, ugly, messy,* and *short* are adjectives.

An **ADVERB** tells how something is done. It modifies a verb and usually ends in "ly." *Modestly, stupidly, greedily,* and *carefully* are adverbs.

A **NOUN** is the name of a person, place, or thing. *Sidewalk, umbrella, bridle, bathtub,* and *nose* are nouns.

A **VERB** is an action word. *Run, pitch, jump,* and *swim* are verbs. Put the verbs in past tense if the directions say PAST TENSE. *Ran, pitched, jumped,* and *swam* are verbs in the past tense.

When we ask for **A PLACE**, we mean any sort of place: a country or city (*Spain, Cleveland*) or a room (*bathroom, kitchen*).

An **EXCLAMATION** or **SILLY WORD** is any sort of funny sound, gasp, grunt, or outcry, like *Wow!, Ouch!, Whomp!, Ick!,* and *Gadzooks!*

When we ask for specific words, like a **NUMBER**, a **COLOR**, an **ANIMAL**, or a **PART OF THE BODY**, we mean a word that is one of those things, like *seven, blue, horse,* or *head*.

When we ask for a **PLURAL**, it means more than one. For example, *cat* pluralized is *cats*.

MAD LIBS® is fun to play with friends, but you can also play it by yourself! To begin with, DO NOT look at the story on the page below. Fill in the blanks on this page with the words called for. Then, using the words you have selected, fill in the blank spaces in the story.

Now you've created your own hilarious MAD LIBS® game!

THE PERFECT SPECIMEN

ADJECTIVE _____

PART OF THE BODY _____

NOUN _____

ADJECTIVE _____

PART OF THE BODY _____

PART OF THE BODY _____

ADJECTIVE _____

PART OF THE BODY _____

TYPE OF FOOD _____

CELEBRITY (MALE) _____

NOUN _____

PART OF THE BODY _____

PLURAL NOUN _____

PART OF THE BODY _____

PLURAL NOUN _____

ADJECTIVE _____

CELEBRITY (MALE) _____

MAD LIBS
THE PERFECT SPECIMEN

The key to the _____ man is his _____.
                      ADJECTIVE   PART OF THE BODY

Without it, he's just another unemployed _____. He
                                              NOUN

should have a/an _____ mind, broad _____,
                    ADJECTIVE   PART OF THE BODY

athletic _____, _____ eyes, a thick
            PART OF THE BODY   ADJECTIVE

_____, mouth as juicy as a/an _____. He
   PART OF THE BODY   TYPE OF FOOD

should also have style as hip as _____, sense of
                                      CELEBRITY (MALE)

of humor as sharp as a/an _____, a/an _____
                              NOUN   PART OF THE BODY

that's not bigger than yours, hands as big as _____,
                                                  PLURAL NOUN

and a/an _____ that goes on forever.
            PART OF THE BODY

But under no circumstances should he ever be unkind to four-legged

_____ or be impolite to your _____
   PLURAL NOUN   ADJECTIVE

mother. Really, you're just looking for a dead ringer for

_____. Is that too much to ask?
   CELEBRITY (MALE)

From KEEPERS AND LOSERS MAD LIBS® • Copyright © 2005 by Chamberlain Bros.,
a division of Penguin Group (USA), Inc., 375 Hudson Street, New York, New York 10014.

MAD LIBS® is fun to play with friends, but you can also play it by yourself! To begin with, DO NOT look at the story on the page below. Fill in the blanks on this page with the words called for. Then, using the words you have selected, fill in the blank spaces in the story.

Now you've created your own hilarious MAD LIBS® game!

THE METROSEXUAL

CELEBRITY (FEMALE) _____

TYPE OF LIQUID _____

PART OF THE BODY_____

CELEBRITY (MALE)_____

NOUN _____

NOUN _____

NUMBER _____

TYPE OF LIQUID _____

PLURAL NOUN _____

NUMBER _____

TYPE OF EVENT _____

TYPE OF SPORT _____

NOUN _____

OCCUPATION _____

MAD●LIBS®
THE METROSEXUAL

While he professes to love _____, the pieces don't
CELEBRITY (FEMALE)

add up. Check the following list to see if your man is a little too

into himself.

- Uses lots of _____ in his hair before going out
  TYPE OF LIQUID

- Suspect he waxes his _____
  PART OF THE BODY

- Starts grooving when he hears _____
  CELEBRITY (MALE)

- Knows the difference between his _____ and
  NOUN

  his _____
  NOUN

- Showers _____ times a day and has been known to
  NUMBER

  take a bath in _____
  TYPE OF LIQUID

- Owns more than ten pairs of _____
  PLURAL NOUN

- Can tie his necktie _____ ways
  NUMBER

- Attends _____ instead of _____
  TYPE OF EVENT   TYPE OF SPORT

- Buys his _____ based on its color, not its performance
  NOUN

- Secretly wants to be a hair _____
  OCCUPATION

From KEEPERS AND LOSERS MAD LIBS® • Copyright © 2005 by Chamberlain Bros.,
a division of Penguin Group (USA), Inc., 375 Hudson Street, New York, New York 10014.

MAD LIBS® is fun to play with friends, but you can also play it by yourself! To begin with, DO NOT look at the story on the page below. Fill in the blanks on this page with the words called for. Then, using the words you have selected, fill in the blank spaces in the story.

Now you've created your own hilarious MAD LIBS® game!

HIS JOB

VERB ENDING IN "S" _____

NOUN _____

ADJECTIVE _____

ADJECTIVE _____

NUMBER _____

VERB ENDING IN "S" _____

NOUN _____

ADVERB _____

PLURAL NOUN _____

PLURAL NOUN _____

ADJECTIVE _____

ADJECTIVE _____

PLURAL NOUN _____

ADJECTIVE _____

NOUN _____

NOUN _____

MAD LIBS®
HIS JOB

He _____ his job, but it drives you out of your
    VERB ENDING IN "S"

_____. However, it gives him a/an _____ sense
    NOUN   ADJECTIVE

of identity, not to mention a/an _____ bank balance. On
                                  ADJECTIVE

the other hand, he works _____ hours and is often stressed
                           NUMBER

out when he _____ you, which is once in a blue
            VERB ENDING IN "S"

_____. When you do get together, all he can do is complain
    NOUN

_____ about _____. In fact, he's often
    ADVERB   PLURAL NOUN

carrying _____ in his briefcase to do before bed.
            PLURAL NOUN

You worry about him and suspect he's being overworked

by his _____ boss. But _____ dinners and
       ADJECTIVE   ADJECTIVE

expensive _____ more than make up for his _____
        PLURAL NOUN   ADJECTIVE

behavior. If you don't see him very often, so be it. But he'd better

take you to his office holiday _____, or there will be
                           NOUN

_____ to pay.
    NOUN

MAD LIBS® is fun to play with friends, but you can also play it by yourself! To begin with, DO NOT look at the story on the page below. Fill in the blanks on this page with the words called for. Then, using the words you have selected, fill in the blank spaces in the story.

Now you've created your own hilarious MAD LIBS® game!

MEET THE PARENTS

ADJECTIVE_____

ADJECTIVE_____

NOUN _____

ADJECTIVE_____

NOUN _____

NOUN _____

ADJECTIVE_____

TYPE OF LIQUID _____

ADJECTIVE_____

ADJECTIVE_____

NUMBER _____

COLOR_____

NUMBER _____

NOUN _____

NOUN _____

ADJECTIVE_____

VERB _____

VERB ENDING IN "S"_____

VERB _____

NOUN _____

MAD LIBS
MEET THE PARENTS

After seven _____ weeks, the _____ moment has
             ADJECTIVE   ADJECTIVE

finally arrived. You are meeting his mother and his _____!
              NOUN

As you approach their _____ house, the door opens
         ADJECTIVE

and a woman with a big _____ greets you. It's the
          NOUN

mother. His Dad grabs you around your _____, gives you
           NOUN

a/an _____ hug and pulls you into the house. After a few
   ADJECTIVE

glasses of _____ you sit down to a/an _____
    TYPE OF LIQUID   ADJECTIVE

dinner. The mother is _____ and asks you, "So how
        ADJECTIVE

old are you really? You look like you're _____." Your face
           NUMBER

turns _____ as you mutter, "I'm _____." You don't
    COLOR   NUMBER

know if it's the _____ or the _____, but you
       NOUN   NOUN

are beginning to feel _____. You make your apologies
        ADJECTIVE

and try to _____. The father _____ you on
     VERB   VERB ENDING IN "S"

the cheek. You _____ away, hoping to never see the
        VERB

_____ or his family again.
  NOUN

MAD LIBS® is fun to play with friends, but you can also play it by yourself! To begin with, DO NOT look at the story on the page below. Fill in the blanks on this page with the words called for. Then, using the words you have selected, fill in the blank spaces in the story.

Now you've created your own hilarious MAD LIBS® game!

HIS RIDE

A PLACE _____

NOUN _____

NOUN _____

ADVERB _____

NUMBER _____

VERB _____

ADJECTIVE _____

ADJECTIVE _____

SILLY NOISE (PLURAL) _____

PART OF THE BODY _____

ADVERB _____

NOUN _____

PLURAL NOUN _____

NOUN _____

A PLACE _____

ADVERB _____

ADJECTIVE _____

ADJECTIVE _____

NOUN _____

VERB _____

NOUN _____

MAD LIBS

HIS RIDE

At long last, he's picking you up at your _____ and
<u>A PLACE</u>

you can't wait to see the new _____ he's driving. After all,
<u>NOUN</u>

he talks about it all the time. As he rolls up in the _____,
<u>NOUN</u>

you gasp _____. It looks like he's spent _____
<u>ADVERB</u> <u>NUMBER</u>

dollars on it. You _____ into it and find it _____.
<u>VERB</u> <u>ADJECTIVE</u>

The seats are extraordinarily _____. It makes
<u>ADJECTIVE</u>

_____, and it smells like an old _____.
<u>SILLY NOISE (PLURAL)</u> <u>PART OF THE BODY</u>

"Sweet ride, isn't it?" he asks you _____. "Uh-huh," you
<u>ADVERB</u>

mutter as you hold on to your _____ for dear life. You see
<u>NOUN</u>

_____ coming out of the _____ and
<u>PLURAL NOUN</u> <u>NOUN</u>

pray you arrive at the _____ safely. But then again,
<u>A PLACE</u>

the valet might look at you _____. All of a sudden a/an
<u>ADVERB</u>

_____ noise starts rumbling somewhere and you hear
<u>ADJECTIVE</u>

something _____ hit the ground under you. At the first
<u>ADJECTIVE</u>

_____, you _____ out of his piece of
<u>NOUN</u> <u>VERB</u>

_____ and never look back.
<u>NOUN</u>

From KEEPERS AND LOSERS MAD LIBS® • Copyright © 2005 by Chamberlain Bros.,
a division of Penguin Group (USA), Inc., 375 Hudson Street, New York, New York 10014.

MAD LIBS® is fun to play with friends, but you can also play it by yourself! To begin with, DO NOT look at the story on the page below. Fill in the blanks on this page with the words called for. Then, using the words you have selected, fill in the blank spaces in the story.

Now you've created your own hilarious MAD LIBS® game!

MANNERS 101

ADJECTIVE _____

ADJECTIVE _____

NOUN _____

NOUN _____

VERB ENDING IN "S" _____

PART OF THE BODY _____

TYPE OF FOOD _____

NOUN _____

NOUN _____

NOUN _____

PART OF THE BODY _____

ADJECTIVE _____

OCCUPATION (PLURAL) _____

ADVERB _____

MADLIBS
MANNERS 101

You've come to a/an _____ realization: His manners are
ADJECTIVE

_____. When he picks you up, he leans on the
ADJECTIVE

_____ instead of coming to the _____
NOUN   NOUN

for you. He _____ your mother on the _____
VERB ENDING IN "S"   PART OF THE BODY

when he meets her and insults her _____ to boot. When
TYPE OF FOOD

you go out to dinner, he never opens the _____ for you
NOUN

and always walks into the _____ ahead of you. He has never
NOUN

once pulled out a/an _____ for you and, worst of all, he
NOUN

picks his _____ at the table and gets into _____
PART OF THE BODY   ADJECTIVE

arguments with all the _____. But all in all, he has
OCCUPATION (PLURAL)

potential: He's _____ bright, he's alive and he's
ADVERB

breathing—the perfect gentleman.

MAD LIBS® is fun to play with friends, but you can also play it by yourself! To begin with, DO NOT look at the story on the page below. Fill in the blanks on this page with the words called for. Then, using the words you have selected, fill in the blank spaces in the story.

THIRD DATE

NOUN _____

NOUN _____

ADJECTIVE _____

COLOR _____

NUMBER_____

NOUN _____

ADJECTIVE _____

PLURAL NOUN_____

NOUN _____

NUMBER_____

VERB _____

ADJECTIVE _____

ADJECTIVE _____

NOUN _____

PART OF THE BODY (PLURAL) _____

TYPE OF CONTAINER_____

MAD LIBS
THIRD DATE

On your first date, he rented a/an _____ and took you

NOUN

to a/an expensive _____. On the second date, he got

NOUN

tickets to a sold out concert featuring the _____

ADJECTIVE

__ new band _____ _____. Now

COLOR NUMBER

you are looking forward to the third date and even bought a

new _____ to wear. Unfortunately, he shows up in

NOUN

jeans, and a/an _____ t-shirt, carrying a container

ADJECTIVE

of Chinese _____. You're disappointed when he says

PLURAL NOUN

that he thought the two of you could stay in and watch the newest

release, *Dude, Where's My* _____, *Part* _____.

NOUN NUMBER

You want to _____ out loud. Instead, you invite him

VERB

in and go to change into something more _____.

ADJECTIVE

When you return, the _____ movie is already

ADJECTIVE

playing, and he is sprawled out on the _____, eating with his

NOUN

_____ from the _____. You

PART OF THE BODY (PLURAL) TYPE OF CONTAINER

suddenly realize you're dating your father!

From MAD LIBS® KEEPERS AND LOSERS • Copyright © 2005 by Chamberlain Bros.,
a division of Penguin Group (USA), Inc., New York, 375 Hudson Street, New York, New York 10014.

MAD LIBS® is fun to play with friends, but you can also play it by yourself! To begin with, DO NOT look at the story on the page below. Fill in the blanks on this page with the words called for. Then, using the words you have selected, fill in the blank spaces in the story.

Now you've created your own hilarious MAD LIBS® game!

MAMA'S BOY

ADJECTIVE_____

ADJECTIVE_____

NOUN _____

VERB ENDING IN "S"_____

NUMBER _____

PLURAL NOUN _____

ANIMAL _____

NOUN _____

NOUN _____

NOUN _____

VERB _____

NOUN _____

NOUN _____

VERB _____

MAD LIBS®
MAMA'S BOY

At first you thought his relationship with his mother was

_____, but now you're starting to think that your
 ADJECTIVE

_____ guy might be a little too attached to her
 ADJECTIVE

_____ strings. Here are some signs to look out for:
 NOUN

• He _____ his mother _____ times a day.
 VERB ENDING IN "S"   NUMBER

• She still buys him _____ to wear at the office.
 PLURAL NOUN

• He asked you to take cooking lessons from her, so you could

make his favorite dishes like rack of _____,
 ANIMAL

_____ pie and _____ soup.
 NOUN   NOUN

• She comes over to the _____ every night to
 NOUN

_____ him into _____.
 VERB   NOUN

• He lectured you for an hour when you accidentally lost the

_____ his mother gave him.
 NOUN

• His mother asked him to _____ back home… and
 VERB

he's considering it.

From KEEPERS AND LOSERS MAD LIBS® • Copyright © 2005 by Chamberlain Bros.,
a division of Penguin Group (USA), Inc., 375 Hudson Street, New York, New York 10014.

MAD LIBS® is fun to play with friends, but you can also play it by yourself! To begin with, DO NOT look at the story on the page below. Fill in the blanks on this page with the words called for. Then, using the words you have selected, fill in the blank spaces in the story.

THAT #$%^& TV

ADJECTIVE _____

NOUN _____

VERB _____

ADJECTIVE _____

NOUN _____

ADJECTIVE _____

PLURAL NOUN _____

NOUN _____

NOUN _____

PLURAL NOUN _____

VERB _____

VERB _____

CELEBRITY (MALE) _____

NOUN _____

His new _____ screen TV is driving you up the

ADJECTIVE

_____. You don't even have room to _____.

NOUN   VERB

However, he's in love with the _____ set.

ADJECTIVE

He won't let you lay a/an _____ on it . . . or touch the

NOUN

_____ remote. He watches sports and _____

ADJECTIVE   PLURAL NOUN

24/7, and has become a real couch _____. He has

NOUN

hooked up his _____ to it and can check his _____

NOUN   PLURAL NOUN

from one corner. He likes to _____ computer games on it

VERB

and has recently programmed it to _____ to him in

VERB

a voice that sounds like _____. He just got TiVo® so

CELEBRITY (MALE)

he'll probably never leave the _____ again!

NOUN

MAD LIBS® is fun to play with friends, but you can also play it by yourself! To begin with, DO NOT look at the story on the page below. Fill in the blanks on this page with the words called for. Then, using the words you have selected, fill in the blank spaces in the story.

PICKUP LINES

ADVERB _____

NOUN _____

PART OF THE BODY _____

VERB ENDING IN "ING" _____

NOUN _____

OCCUPATION_____

NOUN _____

PLURAL NOUN_____

PART OF THE BODY (PLURAL) _____

ADJECTIVE _____

NOUN _____

PLURAL NOUN_____

PLURAL NOUN_____

PART OF THE BODY _____

VERB (PAST TENSE) _____

ADJECTIVE _____

MAD LIBS®
PICKUP LINES

Ever heard these before? If so, run away _____!
ADVERB

• Can I buy you a/an _____ or do you just want the money?
NOUN

• Your _____ must be real tired, because you've been
PART OF THE BODY

_____ through my _____ all night long.
VERB ENDING IN "ING"   NOUN

• Your father must have been a/an _____, because he
OCCUPATION

stole the _____ from the _____ and put
NOUN   PLURAL NOUN

them in your _____.
PART OF THE BODY (PLURAL)

• Is it _____ in here, or is it just you?
ADJECTIVE

• Do you have a/an _____? No? How about a date?
NOUN

• Look at all of those _____ and me with no _____!
PLURAL NOUN   PLURAL NOUN

• Do you have a Band-Aid? Because I skinned my _____
PART OF THE BODY

when I _____ for you.
VERB (PAST TENSE)

• I may not be the most _____ guy in the room, but I'm
ADJECTIVE

the only one talking to you!

From KEEPERS AND LOSERS MAD LIBS® • Copyright © 2005 by Chamberlain Bros.,
a division of Penguin Group (USA), Inc., 375 Hudson Street, New York, New York 10014.

MAD LIBS® is fun to play with friends, but you can also play it by yourself! To begin with, DO NOT look at the story on the page below. Fill in the blanks on this page with the words called for. Then, using the words you have selected, fill in the blank spaces in the story.

Now you've created your own hilarious MAD LIBS® game!

THE BREAKUP SOLILOQUY

VERB ENDING IN "ING" _____

VERB _____

ADJECTIVE_____

PLURAL NOUN _____

NOUN _____

ADJECTIVE_____

VERB _____

NOUN _____

VERB _____

ADJECTIVE_____

PLURAL NOUN _____

NOUN _____

VERB ENDING IN "ING" _____

NOUN _____

VERB _____

ADJECTIVE_____

NOUN _____

ADJECTIVE_____

CELEBRITY (MALE)_____

MAD LIBS®
THE BREAKUP SOLILOQUY

This isn't working out. I've enjoyed _____ with you

　　　　　　　　　VERB ENDING IN "ING"

and getting to _____ you, but we come from two

　　　　　　VERB

_____ worlds and want different _____

　ADJECTIVE　　　　　　　　　　　　　　　　PLURAL NOUN

out of life. For instance, I want a family and you want a/an

_____. I want a/an _____ career and

　　NOUN　　　　　　　　　　ADJECTIVE

you want to _____ your _____. I like

　　　　　VERB　　　　　　　　PLURAL NOUN

to _____ with my friends and you enjoy _____

　VERB　　　　　　　　　　　　　　　　　　ADJECTIVE

evenings at home with your collection of _____. You

　　　　　　　　　　　　　　　　　　PLURAL NOUN

hog the _____, you hate _____, and

　　　　NOUN　　　　　　　　VERB ENDING IN "ING"

you barely tolerate my _____. You don't _____

　　　　　　　　　　NOUN　　　　　　　　　　　VERB

my family and you even think I look _____ in my favorite

　　　　　　　　　　　　　　　　ADJECTIVE

_____ and that my haircut is _____.

　　NOUN　　　　　　　　　　　　　　　　ADJECTIVE

This just won't do. I deserve better. I deserve _____. In

　　　　　　　　　　　　　　　　　　　　　CELEBRITY (MALE)

this case, it's not me, it's *you*.

From KEEPERS AND LOSERS MAD LIBS® • Copyright © 2005 by Chamberlain Bros.,
a division of Penguin Group (USA), Inc., 375 Hudson Street, New York, New York 10014.

MAD LIBS® is fun to play with friends, but you can also play it by yourself! To begin with, DO NOT look at the story on the page below. Fill in the blanks on this page with the words called for. Then, using the words you have selected, fill in the blank spaces in the story.

THE SPORTS FAN

NOUN _____

NOUN _____

ADJECTIVE _____

ADJECTIVE _____

CELEBRITY (FEMALE) _____

ADJECTIVE _____

PLURAL NOUN_____

PLURAL NOUN_____

VERB _____

NUMBER_____

PLURAL NOUN_____

NOUN _____

ADVERB _____

PERSON IN ROOM (MALE) _____

VERB ENDNG IN "ING"_____

VERB _____

NOUN _____

MAD LIBS®
THE SPORTS FAN

His favorite sport is _____-ball. He loves to play it and
      NOUN

he loves to watch it. He loves it almost as much as his sport utility

_____. Decked out in bright _____ gear, he looks
 NOUN   ADJECTIVE

_____ on the field. He once pushed _____
ADJECTIVE   CELEBRITY (FEMALE)

at a charity game. He says it was an accident, but you think

otherwise. He's actually _____. He should be, with all the
       ADJECTIVE

money he spends on _____ and fancy _____. He
      PLURAL NOUN   PLURAL NOUN

also likes to _____ it on TV. He has whiled away many
     VERB

a weekend, watching for _____ hours straight and
         NUMBER

eating greasy _____. He forgot to attend a charity _____
    PLURAL NOUN   NOUN

because of a big game and he disappears _____ with
           ADVERB

_____ for tailgate parties and road trips. He polishes
PERSON IN ROOM (MALE)

his high school _____ trophies in the off-season.
     VERB ENDING IN "ING"

Since you just can't _____ him anymore, you've decided
       VERB

to join him. You just bought your own _____ in his team
         NOUN

colors.

MAD LIBS® is fun to play with friends, but you can also play it by yourself! To begin with, DO NOT look at the story on the page below. Fill in the blanks on this page with the words called for. Then, using the words you have selected, fill in the blank spaces in the story.

ISN'T HE ROMANTIC

NOUN _____

PLURAL NOUN _____

ADJECTIVE _____

ADJECTIVE _____

NOUN _____

VERB _____

NOUN _____

PLURAL NOUN _____

ADJECTIVE _____

ADJECTIVE _____

NOUN _____

NOUN _____

ADJECTIVE _____

ADJECTIVE _____

ADJECTIVE _____

MAD LIBS®
ISN'T HE ROMANTIC

You're out having dinner with your girlfriends. They are

complaining that their men sit in front of the _____
                                                        NOUN

watching ESPN, eating _____, and totally ignoring
                              PLURAL NOUN

them. As they finish their _____ list of heartaches,
                                      ADJECTIVE

their eyes turn to you. But what can you say? Your guy is

_____. He gives you a/an _____ and says
     ADJECTIVE   NOUN

"I _____ you" every day. He never forgets your
          VERB

special _____ and always sends you _____
              NOUN   PLURAL NOUN

on your anniversary. He surprises you once a year with

a/an _____ vacation to a/an _____ place.
         ADJECTIVE   ADJECTIVE

And everyone knows he proposed to you while sitting in a/an

_____, gliding down a/an _____ in Venice Italy,
       NOUN   NOUN

while the gondolier sang a/an _____ love song. As you
                                      ADJECTIVE

recall this _____ moment, you can't help but break
                  ADJECTIVE

into a/an _____ smile and offer to pick up the tab....
                ADJECTIVE

MAD LIBS® is fun to play with friends, but you can also play it by yourself! To begin with, DO NOT look at the story on the page below. Fill in the blanks on this page with the words called for. Then, using the words you have selected, fill in the blank spaces in the story.

Now you've created your own hilarious MAD LIBS® game!

THE COOKOUT

TYPE OF EVENT _____

CELEBRITY (MALE) _____

ADJECTIVE _____

ANIMAL _____

VERB _____

VERB ENDING IN "S" _____

ADVERB _____

EXCLAMATION _____

ADJECTIVE _____

SILLY NOISE _____

NOUN _____

PART OF THE BODY _____

VERB _____

ADJECTIVE _____

TYPE OF FOOD _____

PART OF THE BODY _____

EXCLAMATION _____

SILLY NOISE _____

VERB _____

JUST GOOD
PLAIN MEAT

MAD LIBS
THE COOKOUT

It's summer, time for his _____. He's invited his
                              TYPE OF EVENT

friends, coworkers, and even _____ to sample his
                                CELEBRITY (MALE)

_____ dish: barbecued _____. People
ADJECTIVE   ANIMAL

_____ around the grill until he _____
VERB   VERB ENDING IN "S"

a hunk of meat onto their plates. One guest chews _____
                                                        ADVERB

for a long time; when he swallows, he says, "_____!" It
                                                EXCLAMATION

does seem to be rather _____. Another guest swallows
                              ADJECTIVE

too quickly and starts making a/an _____ and waving her
                                        SILLY NOISE

arms. She's choking! Your man throws down his _____ and
                                                    NOUN

grabs her _____ to perform the Heimlich _____.
          PART OF THE BODY   VERB

He gives it a/an _____ squeeze, and the offending
                  ADJECTIVE

_____ flies out of her mouth, hitting you directly in
TYPE OF FOOD

the _____. "_____!" you cry, as she
      PART OF THE BODY   EXCLAMATION

murmurs "_____" and starts to _____ your
          SILLY NOISE   VERB

guy a bit too long. This party is *over*.

MAD LIBS® is fun to play with friends, but you can also play it by yourself! To begin with, DO NOT look at the story on the page below. Fill in the blanks on this page with the words called for. Then, using the words you have selected, fill in the blank spaces in the story.

Now you've created your own hilarious MAD LIBS® game!

THE SOPHISTICATE

PLURAL NOUN _____

PLURAL NOUN _____

TYPE OF LIQUID _____

TYPE OF CONTAINER _____

VERB _____

NOUN _____

ARTICLE OF CLOTHING (PLURAL) _____

FOREIGN COUNTRY _____

PLURAL NOUN _____

OCCUPATION _____

PLURAL NOUN _____

PLURAL NOUN _____

CELEBRITY (MALE) _____

ADJECTIVE _____

VERB _____

MAD LIBS
THE SOPHISTICATE

He prefers reading _____ to playing _____.
PLURAL NOUN   PLURAL NOUN

He'd rather drink _____ than anything else, and only
            TYPE OF LIQUID

out of a/an _____. He loves the touch of silk and will
        TYPE OF CONTAINER

_____ at the sight of a well-made _____. He
VERB   NOUN

is extremely particular about folding his _____
                                 ARTICLE OF CLOTHING (PLURAL)

in something resembling origami. He speaks the native tongue of

_____, all the better to procure rare _____.
FOREIGN COUNTRY   PLURAL NOUN

He tried his hand at being a/an _____ but decided it
                        OCCUPATION

was beneath him. Instead, he spends his day in pursuit of

_____ and _____. Of course, he's as poor
PLURAL NOUN   PLURAL NOUN

as _____ was in his _____ days. If only he had the
CELEBRITY (MALE)   ADJECTIVE

means to _____ in the style to which he's become
          VERB

accustomed!

From KEEPERS AND LOSERS MAD LIBS® • Copyright © 2005 by Chamberlain Bros.,
a division of Penguin Group (USA), Inc., 375 Hudson Street, New York, New York 10014.

MAD LIBS® is fun to play with friends, but you can also play it by yourself! To begin with, DO NOT look at the story on the page below. Fill in the blanks on this page with the words called for. Then, using the words you have selected, fill in the blank spaces in the story.

A FEW DEAL BREAKERS

NOUN _____

PLURAL NOUN_____

TYPE OF LIQUID_____

NOUN _____

SILLY NOISE_____

PLURAL NOUN_____

VEHICLE _____

NOUN _____

NOUN _____

CELEBRITY (FEMALE) _____

PLURAL NOUN_____

OCCUPATION (PLURAL)_____

MAD LIBS
A FEW DEAL BREAKERS

- Loves his pet _____ more than his mother
  NOUN

- Obsessively catalogues and updates his collection of _____
  PLURAL NOUN

- Slathers his hair with _____
  TYPE OF LIQUID

- Dresses his dog in a purple _____
  NOUN

- Says "_____" when the two of you snuggle
  SILLY NOISE

- Spends too much money on extravagant _____
  PLURAL NOUN

- Sleeps in a bed that resembles a 20-year-old_____
  VEHICLE

- His _____ is smaller than yours
  NOUN

- Travels to a foreign _____ regularly and has never invited

you along

- Looks like _____ when his hair gets too long
  CELEBRITY (FEMALE)

- Is mean to _____, as well as _____
  PLURAL NOUN   OCCUPATION (PLURAL)

From KEEPERS AND LOSERS MAD LIBS® • Copyright © 2005 by Chamberlain Bros.,
a division of Penguin Group (USA), Inc., 375 Hudson Street, New York, New York 10014.

MAD LIBS® is fun to play with friends, but you can also play it by yourself! To begin with, DO NOT look at the story on the page below. Fill in the blanks on this page with the words called for. Then, using the words you have selected, fill in the blank spaces in the story.

Now you've created your own hilarious MAD LIBS® game!

HIS FRIENDS

NOUN _____

NUMBER _____

VERB ENDING IN "ING" _____

PLURAL NOUN _____

ADJECTIVE_____

TYPE OF FOOD _____

NOUN _____

ADJECTIVE_____

NOUN _____

PLURAL NOUN _____

PERSON IN ROOM (MALE)_____

ADJECTIVE_____

NOUN _____

COLOR_____

TYPE OF FOOD_____

ADJECTIVE_____

MAD LIBS
HIS FRIENDS

You can tell a lot by the _____ a person keeps, and
NOUN

this is certainly true about your man. He has _____
NUMBER

good buddies, but a few really stand out. His best friend will

always talk him into _____ your dates because of a
VERB ENDING IN "ING"

"crisis." Another guy is in love with you and constantly sends you

_____ on the sly. His most _____ pal
PLURAL NOUN   ADJECTIVE

treats you like week-old _____ and ignores you
TYPE OF FOOD

whenever you see him. One dude moves in on weekends during

_____ season. He's _____ and litters your
NOUN   ADJECTIVE

man's _____ with _____. And then
NOUN   PLURAL NOUN.

there's _____! He's tall, _____, and handsome,
PERSON IN ROOM (MALE)   ADJECTIVE

and his body is built like a brick _____. If you weren't
NOUN

dating your man, you'd be all over him like _____
COLOR

on _____.
TYPE OF FOOD

Aren't friends _____?
ADJECTIVE

From KEEPERS AND LOSERS MAD LIBS® • Copyright © 2005 by Chamberlain Bros.,
a division of Penguin Group (USA), Inc., 375 Hudson Street, New York, New York 10014.

MAD LIBS® is fun to play with friends, but you can also play it by yourself! To begin with, DO NOT look at the story on the page below. Fill in the blanks on this page with the words called for. Then, using the words you have selected, fill in the blank spaces in the story.

Now you've created your own hilarious MAD LIBS® game!

HIS HEALTH REPORT

ADJECTIVE_____

NOUN _____

NOUN _____

PLURAL NOUN _____

ADVERB_____

NUMBER _____

COLOR_____

VERB _____

PLURAL NOUN _____

PLURAL NOUN _____

NOUN _____

PLURAL NOUN _____

NOUN _____

NOUN _____

CELEBRITY (FEMALE) _____

ADJECTIVE_____

MAD LIBS

HIS HEALTH REPORT

He looks fit, but he's a hypochondriac who makes _____
ADJECTIVE

noises just walking to the _____. He drinks too
NOUN

much a liquid_____, eats too little _____, and exercises
NOUN   PLURAL NOUN

_____ . His body fat is _____ percent and
ADVERB   NUMBER

you're afraid he's going to turn _____ one day and
COLOR

keel over. When you _____ together, he becomes winded
VERB

after only a few seconds. He bumps into _____
PLURAL NOUN

regularly and his muscles are tight as _____. He
PLURAL NOUN

starts sneezing and scratching his _____ whenever
NOUN

he's around dusty_____. While he can pick up a/an
PLURAL NOUN

_____ with ease, he can't carry you around a small
NOUN

_____ like you are _____. He's got
NOUN   CELEBRITY (FEMALE)

a problem! A/An _____ checkup is in order.
ADJECTIVE

MAD LIBS® is fun to play with friends, but you can also play it by yourself! To begin with, DO NOT look at the story on the page below. Fill in the blanks on this page with the words called for. Then, using the words you have selected, fill in the blank spaces in the story.

Now you've created your own hilarious MAD LIBS® game!

PARENT POTENTIAL

VERB ENDING IN "S" _____

ADJECTIVE _____

SILLY NOISE _____

NOUN _____

PLURAL NOUN _____

ADJECTIVE _____

PLURAL NOUN _____

PLURAL NOUN _____

NOUN _____

ADJECTIVE _____

VEHICLE _____

ADJECTIVE _____

NOUN _____

VERB _____

VERB _____

ADJECTIVE _____

MAD LIBS
PARENT POTENTIAL

Should he be the father of your children? Let's look at the evidence:

He _____ when he spies a/an _____

VERB ENDING IN "S" — ADJECTIVE

baby, then says, "_____." He holds infants like they are

SILLY NOISE

a/an _____ full of _____. He is very

NOUN — PLURAL NOUN

_____ with his nieces and _____, buying

ADJECTIVE — PLURAL NOUN

them _____ and making sure they never

PLURAL NOUN

watch an R-rated tv _____.But he has no tolerance

NOUN

for a/an _____ baby strapped into a/an _____

ADJECTIVE — VEHICLE

and thinks _____ infants should not be allowed in a

ADJECTIVE

public _____. He once confided to you that "Women should

NOUN

_____ the kids, and men should _____ them

VERB — VERB

once in a while." Overall, he'd probably make a/an _____

ADJECTIVE

daddy.

MAD LIBS® is fun to play with friends, but you can also play it by yourself! To begin with, DO NOT look at the story on the page below. Fill in the blanks on this page with the words called for. Then, using the words you have selected, fill in the blank spaces in the story.

Now you've created your own hilarious MAD LIBS® game!

EMOTIONAL RESCUE

OCCUPATION _____

VERB ENDING IN "S" _____

NUMBER _____

ADJECTIVE _____

TYPE OF FOOD _____

VERB ENDING IN "S" _____

TYPE OF CONTAINER (PLURAL) _____

NOUN _____

ADJECTIVE _____

OCCUPATION _____

NOUN _____

PART OF THE BODY _____

FOREIGN COUNTRY _____

VERB ENDING IN "ING" _____

The best thing he could do is see an accredited _____.
OCCUPATION

as soon as possible. All he does is blather on about how much he

_____ his job and how he has _____
VERB ENDING IN "S"   NUMBER

friends and how his _____ girlfriends are as nutty
ADJECTIVE

as _____ and how his family _____
TYPE OF FOOD   VERB EDING IN "S"

him up. In other words, he talks . . . a lot. He dumps his

_____ on you rather than seeking a professional
TYPE OF CONTAINER (PLURAL)

_____. And you're tired of it. While you're enabling his
NOUN

_____ behavior, you're also playing _____.
ADJECTIVE   OCCUPATION

You've started counting the minutes it takes him to ask about your

_____. You often want to claw your _____
NOUN   PART OF THE BODY

off while listening to him wax narcissistic. Maybe it's time to move

to _____. That way, you won't be able to understand
FOREIGN COUNTRY

your new boyfriend when he starts ranting and _____.
VERB EDING IN "ING"

MAD LIBS® is fun to play with friends, but you can also play it by yourself! To begin with, DO NOT look at the story on the page below. Fill in the blanks on this page with the words called for. Then, using the words you have selected, fill in the blank spaces in the story.

A FEW OF HIS FAVORITE THINGS

NOUN _____

EXCLAMATION _____

PERSON IN ROOM (FEMALE) _____

NOUN _____

PERSON IN ROOM (FEMALE) _____

ARTICLE OF CLOTHING _____

OCCUPATION _____

TYPE OF LIQUID _____

NOUN _____

NOUN _____

SMALL CITY _____

SOMETHING ALIVE _____

NOUN _____

NOUN _____

SILLY NOISE _____

NUMBER _____

MAD LIBS
A FEW OF HIS
FAVORITE THINGS

If his _____ was on fire, these are the things your guy
NOUN

would grab as he's screaming "_____!" at the top of
EXCLAMATION

his lungs:

- A signed photo of _____
PERSON IN ROOM (FEMALE)

- The _____ he inherited from _____
NOUN   PERSON IN ROOM (FEMALE)

- A/An _____ from his college years
ARTICLE OF CLOTHING

- The paperwork that proves he's a/an _____
OCCUPATION

- The aged _____ he keeps in his climate-controlled
TYPE OF LIQUID

_____
NOUN

- The purple _____ from his trip to_____
NOUN   SMALL CITY

- The _____ he keeps in a/an_____
SOMETHING ALIVE   NOUN

- His junior-high _____
NOUN

- The cell phone that sounds like _____
SILLY NOISE

- The shoes he bought for _____ dollars
NUMBER

- And, of course, you

Adult
MAD LIBS®

World's Greatest Word Game

DYSFUNCTIONAL FAMILY THERAPY MAD LIBS

By Roger Price and Leonard Stern

PSS!
PRICE STERN SLOAN

ROADSIDE AMUSEMENTS
an imprint of
CHAMBERLAIN BROS.
Published by the Penguin Group
Price Stern Sloan, a division of Penguin Group for Young Readers
Penguin Group (USA) Inc., 375 Hudson Street, New York, New York 10014, USA
Penguin Group (Canada), 90 Eglinton Avenue East, Suite 700,
Toronto, Ontario M4P 2Y3, Canada
(a division of Pearson Penguin Canada Inc.)
Penguin Books Ltd, 80 Strand, London WC2R 0RL, England
Penguin Ireland, 25 St Stephen's Green, Dublin 2, Ireland (a division of Penguin Books Ltd)
Penguin Group (Australia), 250 Camberwell Road, Camberwell, Victoria 3124, Australia
(a division of Pearson Australia Group Pty Ltd)
Penguin Books India Pvt Ltd, 11 Community Centre, Panchsheel Park,
New Delhi—110 017, India
Penguin Group (NZ), Cnr Airborne and Rosedale Roads,
Albany, Auckland 1310, New Zealand (a division of Pearson New Zealand Ltd)
Penguin Books (South Africa) (Pty) Ltd, 24 Sturdee Avenue,
Rosebank, Johannesburg 2196, South Africa

Penguin Books Ltd, Registered Offices: 80 Strand, London WC2R 0RL, England

An application has been submitted to register this book with the Library of Congress.

ISBN 1-59609-181-9

Printed in the United States of America

PSS! and MAD LIBS are registered trademarks of Penguin Group (USA) Inc.

MAD ☺ LIBS®

INSTRUCTIONS

MAD LIBS® is a game for people who don't like games!
It can be played by one, two, three, four, or forty.

• RIDICULOUSLY SIMPLE DIRECTIONS

In this tablet you will find stories containing blank spaces where words are left out. One player, the **READER**, selects one of these stories. The **READER** does not tell anyone what the story is about. Instead, he/she asks the other players, the **WRITERS**, to give him/her words. These words are used to fill in the blank spaces in the story.

• TO PLAY

The **READER** asks each **WRITER** in turn to call out a word—an adjective or a noun or whatever the space calls for—and uses them to fill in the blank spaces in the story. The result is a **MAD LIBS®** game.

When the **READER** then reads the completed **MAD LIBS®** game to the other players, they will discover that they have written a story that is fantastic, screamingly funny, shocking, silly, crazy, or just plain dumb—depending upon which words each **WRITER** called out.

• EXAMPLE (*Before* and *After*)

"_____!" he said _____
      EXCLAMATION   ADVERB

as he jumped into his convertible _____ and
                                        NOUN

drove off with his _____ wife.
                       ADJECTIVE

"*Ouch*_____!" he said *Stupidly*_____
      EXCLAMATION   ADVERB

as he jumped into his convertible *cat*_____ and
                                      NOUN

drove off with his *brave*_____ wife.
                       ADJECTIVE

MAD LIBS®
QUICK REVIEW

In case you have forgotten what adjectives, adverbs, nouns, and verbs are, here is a quick review:

An **ADJECTIVE** describes something or somebody. *Lumpy, soft, ugly, messy,* and *short* are adjectives.

An **ADVERB** tells how something is done. It modifies a verb and usually ends in "ly." *Modestly, stupidly, greedily,* and *carefully* are adverbs.

A **NOUN** is the name of a person, place, or thing. *Sidewalk, umbrella, bridle, bathtub,* and *nose* are nouns.

A **VERB** is an action word. *Run, pitch, jump,* and *swim* are verbs. Put the verbs in past tense if the directions say PAST TENSE. *Ran, pitched, jumped,* and *swam* are verbs in the past tense.

When we ask for **A PLACE**, we mean any sort of place: a country or city *(Spain, Cleveland)* or a room *(bathroom, kitchen).*

An **EXCLAMATION** or **SILLY WORD** is any sort of funny sound, gasp, grunt, or outcry, like *Wow!, Ouch!, Whomp!, Ick!,* and *Gadzooks!*

When we ask for specific words, like a **NUMBER**, a **COLOR**, an **ANIMAL**, or a **PART OF THE BODY**, we mean a word that is one of those things, like *seven, blue, horse,* or *head.*

When we ask for a **PLURAL**, it means more than one. For example, *cat* pluralized is *cats.*

MAD LIBS® is fun to play with friends, but you can also play it by yourself! To begin with, DO NOT look at the story on the page below. Fill in the blanks on this page with the words called for. Then, using the words you have selected, fill in the blank spaces in the story.

Now you've created your own hilarious MAD LIBS® game!

QUIZ

NOUN_____

ADJECTIVE _____

NOUN_____

NOUN_____

NOUN_____

VERB _____

NOUN_____

ADJECTIVE _____

ADJECTIVE _____

NOUN_____

MAD LIBS®
QUIZ

How does one know if one's _____ is dysfunctional?
NOUN

Here's a/an _____ quiz to help you find out:
ADJECTIVE

1. Has a/an _____ ever ignored you for months at a time?
NOUN

2. Do you already know that a certain _____ will
NOUN

   make a pass at your older _____ during the next
   NOUN

   family gathering?

3. Did your parents ever _____ in public?
   VERB

4. Are you afraid to introduce your _____ to your
   NOUN

   mother, for fear of being embarrassed?

If you answered yes to any of these _____ questions,
ADJECTIVE

then the Cleavers you're not. Counseling may help to make you feel

_____, but at this stage you may just prefer a nice
ADJECTIVE

_____ lobotomy.
NOUN

MAD LIBS® is fun to play with friends, but you can also play it by yourself! To begin with, DO NOT look at the story on the page below. Fill in the blanks on this page with the words called for. Then, using the words you have selected, fill in the blank spaces in the story.

Now you've created your own hilarious MAD LIBS® game!

LONG CAR RIDES

NOUN_____

NOUN_____

ADVERB _____

NOUN_____

PERSON IN ROOM (FEMALE) _____

ADJECTIVE _____

NOUN_____

NOUN_____

VERB ENDING IN "ING" _____

NOUN_____

ADJECTIVE _____

PART OF THE BODY _____

NOUN_____

MAD LIBS®

LONG CAR RIDES

While driving along the interstate _____, my sister

NOUN

starts poking me with her _____. When I ask her to

NOUN

stop, she says _____, "You can't tell me what to do.

ADVERB

You're not my _____." So I say, "Mom, will you please tell

NOUN

_____ to stop poking me?" But my mother ignores

PERSON IN ROOM (FEMALE)

my _____ plea. "Dad?" I appeal to the king of the

ADJECTIVE

_____. He turns around with a big _____

NOUN   NOUN

on his face and warns, "If you kids don't knock it off and stop

_____ , I will turn this _____ around

VERB ENDING IN "ING"   NOUN

and head right back home!" After a moment of _____ silence,

ADJECTIVE

my sister whispers into my _____, " Look what you

PART OF THE BODY

did. Now we're going to have a terrible _____!"

NOUN

MAD LIBS® is fun to play with friends, but you can also play it by yourself! To begin with, DO NOT look at the story on the page below. Fill in the blanks on this page with the words called for. Then, using the words you have selected, fill in the blank spaces in the story.

Now you've created your own hilarious MAD LIBS® game!

CASE HISTORY:
THE SPOILED CHILD

PLURAL NOUN _____

ADJECTIVE _____

GEOGRAPHIC LOCATION _____

NOUN _____

NOUN _____

VERB (PAST TENSE) _____

NOUN _____

ADJECTIVE _____

SMALL CITY _____

ADJECTIVE _____

NOUN _____

PLURAL NOUN _____

NOUN _____

NOUN _____

MAD LIBS®
CASE HISTORY:
THE SPOILED CHILD

Spoiled children constantly demand new _____ to
_____PLURAL NOUN_____

play with, as they are never satisfied with what they have. History's

most _____ example is Henry VIII. Discontented with his first
___ADJECTIVE___

wife, Catherine of _____, Henry divorced her and
_____GEOGRAPHIC LOCATION_____

wed Anne Boleyn. But she had a melancholy _____,
_____NOUN_____

so he executed her. His next _____, Jane Seymour,
_____NOUN_____

_____ while giving birth, which made Henry cry like a/an
VERB (PAST TENSE)

_____. He got over it by ordering a new bride from
_____NOUN_____

a/an _____ country. Unfortunately, when Anne of
_____ADJECTIVE_____

_____ arrived, Henry screamed that he found her to be too
SMALL CITY

_____, so he set her aside and married Katherine Howard.
ADJECTIVE

However, she cheated on him so he chopped off her _____.
_____NOUN_____

Finally, there was Catherine Parr, the last of his _____,
_____PLURAL NOUN_____

who survived him. Henry was a spoiled _____ who
_____NOUN_____

grew up to become an even more spoiled _____.
_____NOUN_____

Someone should have administered a royal time-out!

From ADULT MAD LIBS® DYSFUNCTIONAL FAMILY THERAPY • Copyright © 2005 by Roadside Amusements,
a division of Penguin Group (USA) Inc., 375 Hudson Street, New York, New York 10014.

MAD LIBS® is fun to play with friends, but you can also play it by yourself! To begin with, DO NOT look at the story on the page below. Fill in the blanks on this page with the words called for. Then, using the words you have selected, fill in the blank spaces in the story.

Now you've created your own hilarious MAD LIBS® game!

FUN FAMILY PICNIC

NOUN_____

ADJECTIVE _____

NOUN_____

NOUN_____

NOUN_____

NOUN_____

NOUN_____

VERB _____

NOUN_____

NOUN_____

PLURAL NOUN_____

NOUN_____

PART OF THE BODY _____

ADVERB _____

PART OF THE BODY (PLURAL) _____

PLURAL NOUN_____

ADJECTIVE _____

NOUN_____

PLURAL NOUN_____

NOUN_____

MAD LIBS®

FUN FAMILY PICNIC

As usual, our family _____ was a/an _____
NOUN   ADJECTIVE

disaster. Mom packed _____ sandwiches and _____
                          NOUN   NOUN

salad, and Dad brought a volleyball and a/an _____.
                                                       NOUN

Once we got to the _____ grounds, my brother started
                          NOUN

shooting me with a water _____. But when I screamed,
                                NOUN

"_____!" my mom got mad and said, "You just calm
      VERB

down, young _____." Dad was having some trouble
                    NOUN

setting up the _____ net, so I offered to help, but he
                     NOUN

shouted at the top of his _____, "Just stay out of the
                                PLURAL NOUN

_____!" Then I went to give a/an _____
      NOUN   PART OF THE BODY

to Mom. "Well, it's about time somebody offered to help," she said

_____, and then rolled her _____. I spent
      ADVERB   PART OF THE BODY (PLURAL)

the rest of the day eating Mom's _____ (which had
                                        PLURAL NOUN

become _____ in the sun) and watching Dad fight with the
            ADJECTIVE

_____. I wish we could be more like normal _____
      NOUN   PLURAL NOUN

and spend weekends watching reruns on the _____.
                                                  NOUN

MAD LIBS® is fun to play with friends, but you can also play it by yourself! To begin with, DO NOT look at the story on the page below. Fill in the blanks on this page with the words called for. Then, using the words you have selected, fill in the blank spaces in the story.

Now you've created your own hilarious MAD LIBS® game!

THE BRADY BUNCH

NOUN_____

PLURAL NOUN_____

OCCUPATION_____

NOUN_____

ANIMAL_____

NOUN_____

PLURAL NOUN_____

NOUN_____

ADJECTIVE _____

NOUN_____

OCCUPATION_____

NOUN_____

VERB _____

ADJECTIVE _____

PLURAL NOUN_____

NOUN_____

NOUN_____

ADJECTIVE _____

MAD LIBS®
THE BRADY BUNCH

Growing up, I envied the Brady _____. Carol and
                                    NOUN

Mike Brady each had three _____, plus a/an
                              PLURAL NOUN

_____ and a/an _____ named
   OCCUPATION   NOUN

_____. They all lived together as one big, happy
   ANIMAL

_____. (I can still remember their silly _____
   NOUN   PLURAL NOUN

clear as a/an _____.) On one _____
                  NOUN   ADJECTIVE

episode, Jan bought a/an _____ and actually
                              NOUN

wore it to a party. On another, Marcia developed a crush on her

_____. And who can forget the time the kids broke
   OCCUPATION

Mom's favorite _____ and tried to _____
                   NOUN   VERB

it back together? In the end, Carol and Mike always learned the truth

and taught the kids a/an _____ lesson. Mike said, "You
                              ADJECTIVE

know, when you tell on your _____, you're
                                PLURAL NOUN

really telling on yourself," and "You have to learn to keep a/an

_____ —nobody likes a tattle_____."
   NOUN   NOUN

Such _____ wisdom!
         ADJECTIVE

From ADULT MAD LIBS® DYSFUNCTIONAL FAMILY THERAPY • Copyright © 2005 by Roadside Amusements,
a division of Penguin Group (USA) Inc., 375 Hudson Street, New York, New York 10014.

MAD LIBS® is fun to play with friends, but you can also play it by yourself! To begin with, DO NOT look at the story on the page below. Fill in the blanks on this page with the words called for. Then, using the words you have selected, fill in the blank spaces in the story.

Now you've created your own hilarious MAD LIBS® game!

THANKSGIVING DAY SURVIVAL

NOUN_____

ADJECTIVE _____

NOUN_____

NOUN_____

NOUN_____

NOUN_____

PLURAL NOUN_____

NUMBER_____

ADJECTIVE _____

NOUN_____

NOUN_____

NUMBER_____

PLURAL NOUN_____

ADJECTIVE _____

Thanksgiving with your _____ can be a/an _____
                NOUN   ADJECTIVE

experience, but you've got to come prepared. Don't just show up at

your parents' _____ expecting everything to be peaches 'n'
                NOUN

_____. Make a plan. To participate, first go to the
     NOUN

kitchen and help your mother cook the gigantic _____
                                        NOUN

she bought. Then greet each individual _____ at the
                                   NOUN

door, take their _____, and seat them at least _____
           PLURAL NOUN   NUMBER

feet away from each other. Start the conversation by asking Dad

about his _____ old days as the _____ of his high-
          ADJECTIVE   NOUN

school _____ team. (Anything to make him forget that
         NOUN

you still owe _____ dollars for your tuition.) It will also
           NUMBER

keep your grandparents from talking, thus sparing you the lecture on

the "outrageous price of _____ these days." Finally—
                 PLURAL NOUN

and please don't overlook this very _____ step—
                             ADJECTIVE

bring proof that you looked for a job in the past week!

MAD LIBS® is fun to play with friends, but you can also play it by yourself! To begin with, DO NOT look at the story on the page below. Fill in the blanks on this page with the words called for. Then, using the words you have selected, fill in the blank spaces in the story.

Now you've created your own hilarious MAD LIBS® game!

MOTHER, MAY I?

PERSON IN ROOM_____

EXCLAMATION _____

ADJECTIVE _____

NOUN_____

NOUN_____

SAME NOUN _____

NOUN_____

NOUN_____

ADJECTIVE _____

NOUN_____

NOUN_____

ADJECTIVE _____

VERB ENDING IN "ING"_____

ADVERB _____

PLURAL NOUN_____

PERSON IN ROOM_____

NOUN_____

MAD LIBS®

MOTHER, MAY I?

_____ asked if I wanted to sleep over and I said,

PERSON IN ROOM

"_____! That sounds _____. But I'll

EXCLAMATION   ADJECTIVE

have to ask my _____ for permission." So I went to

NOUN

Mom and she said, "Go ask your _____." So I asked my

NOUN

_____ and he said, "Ask your _____."

SAME NOUN   NOUN

Exasperated, I said, "Is anyone here capable of making a/an

_____?" Then Dad got mad and said, "Don't get

NOUN

_____ with me, young _____. Now go

ADJECTIVE   NOUN

to your _____." I complained to Mom that this wasn't

NOUN

fair, but she said, "Nobody said life was _____." "Well,

ADJECTIVE

it should be!" I cried, but nobody was _____. I

VERB ENDING IN "ING"

dropped the subject and went away _____, fighting

ADVERB

back _____. The next day, _____ called

PLURAL NOUN   PERSON IN ROOM

and asked me over for dinner. "Ask your _____," my

NOUN

mother said....

MAD LIBS® is fun to play with friends, but you can also play it by yourself! To begin with, DO NOT look at the story on the page below. Fill in the blanks on this page with the words called for. Then, using the words you have selected, fill in the blank spaces in the story.

Now you've created your own hilarious MAD LIBS® game!

HOW TO INTRODUCE YOUR BOYFRIEND

ADJECTIVE _____

ADJECTIVE _____

ADJECTIVE _____

ADJECTIVE _____

NOUN _____

ADJECTIVE _____

PLURAL NOUN _____

NOUN _____

TYPE OF EVENT _____

NOUN _____

NOUN _____

NOUN _____

SAME NOUN _____

NOUN _____

MAD LIBS
HOW TO INTRODUCE
YOUR BOYFRIEND

Will your family scare your _____ new boyfriend
ADJECTIVE

away? Chances are _____ that they will, so you should
ADJECTIVE

take some _____ steps beforehand to ensure a/an
ADJECTIVE

_____ meeting:
ADJECTIVE

1. Encourage your guy to bring a/an _____ for your mother.
NOUN

   (This should guarantee a/an _____ first impression.)
ADJECTIVE

2. If your family has any unusual _____, warn your
PLURAL NOUN

   boyfriend ahead of time.

3. Tell your mother not to discuss your ex-_____ and
NOUN

   how devastated you were when he called off the _____
TYPE OF EVENT

   at the last _____.
NOUN

Finally, don't panic. Your _____ will still love you. After
NOUN

all, he is not dating your _____, he's dating you. (And
NOUN

if he wishes he were dating your _____, then maybe you
SAME NOUN

should be looking for a new _____!)
NOUN

MAD LIBS® is fun to play with friends, but you can also play it by yourself! To begin with, DO NOT look at the story on the page below. Fill in the blanks on this page with the words called for. Then, using the words you have selected, fill in the blank spaces in the story.

Now you've created your own hilarious MAD LIBS® game!

CHRISTMAS

ADJECTIVE _____

ADJECTIVE _____

ADJECTIVE _____

PLURAL NOUN _____

NUMBER _____

ADJECTIVE _____

NOUN _____

ADVERB _____

PLURAL NOUN _____

ADJECTIVE _____

PLURAL NOUN _____

NUMBER _____

VERB ENDING IN "ING" _____

NOUN _____

PLURAL NOUN _____

ADJECTIVE _____

NOUN _____

SAME NOUN _____

SAME NOUN _____

MAD LIBS
CHRISTMAS

Christmas gatherings require you to not only tolerate your

_____ family's _____ company but also
     ADJECTIVE   ADJECTIVE

to exchange _____ _____! You have to
              ADJECTIVE   PLURAL NOUN

spend _____ months' salary on _____
        NUMBER   ADJECTIVE

presents and then smile and appear grateful when you receive

another horrible _____ that only proves _____
            NOUN   ADVERB

that none of your _____ really know you at all.
            PLURAL NOUN

Your mother always buys you _____ pants and
                ADJECTIVE

_____ that are usually _____
   PLURAL NOUN   NUMBER

size(s) too small. Your father always gives you some sort of

_____ kit that ends up collecting dust on the floor of
VERB ENDING IN "ING"

your _____. The worst is your little brother, who buys
     NOUN

you the latest video _____ just so he can borrow
           PLURAL NOUN

them later on. Maybe this year you should make a/an _____
                        ADJECTIVE

new rule: _____ certificates, _____
        NOUN   SAME NOUN

certificates, _____ certificates!
       SAME NOUN

MAD LIBS® is fun to play with friends, but you can also play it by yourself! To begin with, DO NOT look at the story on the page below. Fill in the blanks on this page with the words called for. Then, using the words you have selected, fill in the blank spaces in the story.

Now you've created your own hilarious MAD LIBS® game!

CASE HISTORY: ANGER MANAGEMENT

ADJECTIVE _____

PLURAL NOUN_____

ADJECTIVE _____

NOUN_____

NATIONALITY_____

VERB (PAST TENSE)_____

PLURAL NOUN_____

ADJECTIVE _____

ADJECTIVE _____

ADJECTIVE _____

ADJECTIVE _____

PART OF THE BODY _____

NOUN _____

ADJECTIVE _____

MAD LIBS
CASE HISTORY:
ANGER MANAGEMENT

Alexander the Great was a/an _____ candidate for
                                    ADJECTIVE

anger management, because he employed _____ rather
                                          PLURAL NOUN

than diplomacy to solve problems. Here are a few _____
                                                      ADJECTIVE

examples:

1. A/An _____ once refused to bow to Alexander in the
          NOUN

_____ fashion, so Alexander had him killed.
NATIONALITY

2. Some governors _____ during Alexander's absence,
                      VERB (PAST TENSE)

so he had them killed.

3. After exploring foreign _____ and meeting all kinds
                              PLURAL NOUN

of new and _____ people, he . . . well, you know!
              ADJECTIVE

One can't help but wonder what _____ Alexander
                                    ADJECTIVE

was so angry about—other than the fact that his parents were so

_____. But what I would like to know is: Once it
ADJECTIVE

became clear that young Alex had a/an _____ chip on
                                          ADJECTIVE

his _____ the size of a/an _____,
      PART OF THE BODY   NOUN

whose _____ idea was it to give him his own army?
          ADJECTIVE

MAD LIBS® is fun to play with friends, but you can also play it by yourself! To begin with, DO NOT look at the story on the page below. Fill in the blanks on this page with the words called for. Then, using the words you have selected, fill in the blank spaces in the story.

Now you've created your own hilarious MAD LIBS® game!

FAMILY PLAN

VERB _____

NOUN_____

ADJECTIVE _____

NUMBER_____

ADJECTIVE _____

VERB ENDING IN "ING"_____

VERB (PAST TENSE)_____

ADJECTIVE _____

NOUN_____

ADJECTIVE _____

NOUN_____

PLURAL NOUN_____

NOUN_____

NOUN_____

ADJECTIVE _____

NOUN_____

MAD LIBS
FAMILY PLAN

Well, we bought the "Family _____ Plan" from our
                                         VERB

mobile _____ company. _____ mistake!
              NOUN   ADJECTIVE

At just _____ cents a minute, it seemed like a/an
                  NUMBER

_____ idea. The first call was from my sister saying
      ADJECTIVE

she didn't make the _____ squad at school. She then
                        VERB ENDING IN "ING"

_____ for an hour while I was trying to watch my
      VERB (PAST TENSE)

_____ TV show, *American* _____. Then
      ADJECTIVE   NOUN

my phone rang again and it was my _____ brother,
                                          ADJECTIVE

asking me to pick him up from _____ practice. On
                                        NOUN

the way home, my mother called and asked me to pick up some

_____ at the neighborhood _____, and
      PLURAL NOUN   NOUN

my father called asking where the car was because he had to get to a

very important _____ by six o'clock! I think I might "lose"
                    NOUN

my _____ phone tomorrow and tell the company what
       ADJECTIVE

they can do with their "Family _____"!
                                    NOUN

MAD LIBS® is fun to play with friends, but you can also play it by yourself! To begin with, DO NOT look at the story on the page below. Fill in the blanks on this page with the words called for. Then, using the words you have selected, fill in the blank spaces in the story.

Now you've created your own hilarious MAD LIBS® game!

THINGS MOM ALWAYS SAID

ADJECTIVE _____

NOUN_____

PLURAL NOUN_____

NOUN_____

ADJECTIVE _____

VERB (PAST TENSE)_____

PLURAL NOUN_____

NOUN_____

NOUN_____

NOUN_____

NOUN_____

ADJECTIVE _____

PLURAL NOUN_____

MAD LIBS

THINGS MOM ALWAYS SAID

These are some of the _____ phrases you might,
ADJECTIVE

unfortunately, remember hearing from your mother's _____:
NOUN

• "Well, if the other _____ jumped off the Brooklyn
PLURAL NOUN

_____, would you do it, too?"
NOUN

• "Always wear _____ underwear in case you're in
ADJECTIVE

an accident."

• "I never _____ when I was your age."
VERB (PAST TENSE)

• "Turn on the _____ when you read—you'll go blind."
PLURAL NOUN

• "Don't sit so close to the _____—you'll go blind."
NOUN

• "Don't use your _____ to wipe your face. Always
NOUN

have a clean _____ with you."
NOUN

• "Put on a warm _____—you'll catch cold.
NOUN

I guess when I'm older, I'll impart the same _____
ADJECTIVE

wisdom to my_____.
PLURAL NOUN

MAD LIBS® is fun to play with friends, but you can also play it by yourself! To begin with, DO NOT look at the story on the page below. Fill in the blanks on this page with the words called for. Then, using the words you have selected, fill in the blank spaces in the story.

Now you've created your own hilarious MAD LIBS® game!

MOM'S MEAT LOAF

NUMBER_____

NOUN_____

ADJECTIVE _____

NOUN_____

ADVERB _____

NOUN_____

PLURAL NOUN_____

NOUN_____

NUMBER_____

NUMBER_____

ADJECTIVE _____

PLURAL NOUN_____

ADJECTIVE _____

NOUN_____

PLURAL NOUN_____

NOUN_____

MAD LIBS
MOM'S MEAT LOAF

Ah ... home cookin'. Here's how to make meat loaf exactly like Mom's:

1. In a bowl, combine _____ eggs, a pound of
   <u>NUMBER</u>

   chopped _____, _____ salt, _____
   <u>NOUN</u>   <u>ADJECTIVE</u>   <u>NOUN</u>

   paste, and mustard.

2. Crumble meat over the mixture and mix _____.
   <u>ADVERB</u>

   Sprinkle with onion and _____ crumbs. Mix again
   <u>NOUN</u>

   and then shape into two _____.
   <u>PLURAL NOUN</u>

3. Place loaves in the center of a lightly floured _____.
   <u>NOUN</u>

4. Bake at _____ degrees for _____
   <u>NUMBER</u>   <u>NUMBER</u>

   minutes or until thoroughly _____.
   <u>ADJECTIVE</u>

5. For the sauce, take some melted _____ and whisk
   <u>PLURAL NOUN</u>

   in flour until it's completely _____. Stir in one
   <u>ADJECTIVE</u>

   _____ and two _____. If you like, you
   <u>NOUN</u>   <u>PLURAL NOUN</u>

   can substitute a/an _____ for the flour.
   <u>NOUN</u>

Finally, when your children refuse to eat your creation, storm out of

the room and shout, "Nobody appreciates me!"

From ADULT MAD LIBS® DYSFUNCTIONAL FAMILY THERAPY • Copyright © 2005 by Roadside Amusements, a division of Penguin Group (USA) Inc., 375 Hudson Street, New York, New York 10014.

MAD LIBS® is fun to play with friends, but you can also play it by yourself! To begin with, DO NOT look at the story on the page below. Fill in the blanks on this page with the words called for. Then, using the words you have selected, fill in the blank spaces in the story.

Now you've created your own hilarious MAD LIBS® game!

THE DYSFUNCTIONAL FAMILY MOVIE

NOUN_____

PLURAL NOUN_____

PERSON IN ROOM (MALE) _____

CELEBRITY (MALE) _____

NOUN_____

PLURAL NOUN_____

ADJECTIVE _____

GEOGRAPHIC LOCATION_____

CELEBRITY (FEMALE) _____

PART OF THE BODY _____

NOUN_____

PART OF THE BODY _____

PLURAL NOUN_____

MAD LIBS

THE DYSFUNCTIONAL
FAMILY MOVIE

The _____ *in Winter* features a dysfunctional family of

NOUN

royal _____. The year is 1183 and the film centers

PLURAL NOUN

on King _____ the Second, played by

PERSON IN ROOM (MALE)

_____, who must decide which of his sons will

CELEBRITY (MALE)

take over his royal _____. He summons the three

NOUN

_____, who are all extremely greedy, evil, and

PLURAL NOUN

_____. But even worse is their mother, Queen Eleanor

ADJECTIVE

of _____, played by _____, who

GEOGRAPHIC LOCATION · CELEBRITY (FEMALE)

has a/an _____ of stone. She's especially angry at the

PART OF THE BODY

king because he (1) threw her in prison, and (2) had an affair with

a/an _____ behind her _____! It's

NOUN · PART OF THE BODY

a relief to know that modern royal families don't have to deal with

_____ like these anymore . . . er, never mind!

PLURAL NOUN

MAD LIBS® is fun to play with friends, but you can also play it by yourself! To begin with, DO NOT look at the story on the page below. Fill in the blanks on this page with the words called for. Then, using the words you have selected, fill in the blank spaces in the story.

Now you've created your own hilarious MAD LIBS® game!

TALKING

PLURAL NOUN _____

NOUN _____

ADVERB _____

ADJECTIVE _____

ADJECTIVE _____

NOUN _____

NUMBER _____

ADJECTIVE _____

NOUN _____

ADJECTIVE _____

NOUN _____

NOUN _____

NOUN _____

MAD LIBS®
TALKING

Talking is something that dysfunctional _____ should
PLURAL NOUN

never attempt to do, but there are times when it cannot be avoided,

such as at a family _____. The secret to getting through
NOUN

one of these "get-togethers" is to tell everyone how you are without

_____ giving away any _____ information.
ADVERB ADJECTIVE

(That way, nothing too _____ can get back to your mother.)
ADJECTIVE

You are obligated to chat with each _____ for only
NOUN

_____ minutes, and then it's considered _____
NUMBER ADJECTIVE

to take your leave and escape to the next _____. First,
NOUN

make sure the television is on, if possible, to break the _____
ADJECTIVE

silence. When you see your aunt, compliment her on her new

_____ and ask where she got it. Finally, prepare an
NOUN

emergency phrase, in case someone asks about your _____—
NOUN

something like, "Does anyone know who got eliminated on *American*

_____ last night?"
NOUN

From ADULT MAD LIBS® DYSFUNCTIONAL FAMILY THERAPY • Copyright © 2005 by Roadside Amusements, a division of Penguin Group (USA) Inc., 375 Hudson Street, New York, New York 10014.

MAD LIBS® is fun to play with friends, but you can also play it by yourself! To begin with, DO NOT look at the story on the page below. Fill in the blanks on this page with the words called for. Then, using the words you have selected, fill in the blank spaces in the story.

Now you've created your own hilarious MAD LIBS® game!

SCHOOL COUNSELOR

NOUN_____

NOUN_____

PLURAL NOUN_____

ADJECTIVE _____

PLURAL NOUN_____

ADJECTIVE _____

PLURAL NOUN_____

PERSON IN ROOM (FEMALE) _____

NOUN_____

PART OF THE BODY _____

PLURAL NOUN_____

ADJECTIVE _____

NOUN_____

NUMBER_____

NOUN_____

NOUN_____

MAD LIBS®
SCHOOL COUNSELOR

Throughout my thirty-year career as a high-school guidance

_____, I've worked with just about every kind of
NOUN

dysfunctional _____. I've seen teenagers act like
NOUN

spoiled _____ just to get attention, I've seen
PLURAL NOUN

_____ children with neurotic _____,
ADJECTIVE   PLURAL NOUN

and I've seen _____ things happen to good
ADJECTIVE

_____. My greatest success story involved a young
PLURAL NOUN

lady named _____, who was what we in the
PERSON IN THE ROOM (FEMALE)

business call a/an "_____-maniac." (She had a kind
NOUN

_____, but her self-definition was centered entirely
PART OF THE BODY

on _____.) With her _____ behavior
PLURAL NOUN   ADJECTIVE

patterns, I was afraid she would end up in what we call a "Vicious

_____." I worked with her for _____
NOUN   NUMBER

years, teaching her to value her _____ more. Eventually she
NOUN

grew up to become a strong, independent _____....
NOUN

And now she doesn't return my phone calls.

From ADULT MAD LIBS® DYSFUNCTIONAL FAMILY THERAPY • Copyright © 2005 by Roadside Amusements, a division of Penguin Group (USA) Inc., 375 Hudson Street, New York, New York 10014.

MAD LIBS® is fun to play with friends, but you can also play it by yourself! To begin with, DO NOT look at the story on the page below. Fill in the blanks on this page with the words called for. Then, using the words you have selected, fill in the blank spaces in the story.

Now you've created your own hilarious MAD LIBS® game!

SKI VACATION

ADJECTIVE _____

ADJECTIVE _____

NOUN_____

PLURAL NOUN_____

NOUN_____

NOUN_____

NOUN_____

NOUN_____

ADJECTIVE _____

NOUN_____

NOUN_____

NOUN_____

NOUN_____

MAD LIBS®
SKI VACATION

None of us had ever gone skiing before, but Dad insisted that it

was _____ fun and we were going to have a/an
ADJECTIVE

_____ weekend. I've heard that before. We spent
ADJECTIVE

the first day in the shops because Mom wanted to look like a/an

_____ on the slopes. The second day, she went back
NOUN

because she forgot to buy _____ to go with her new
PLURAL NOUN

_____, so Dad and I left without her. At the foot of the
NOUN

mountain, our car got a flat _____ and we waited four
NOUN

hours for an auto _____ truck to come along. By the
NOUN

time the _____ was fixed, we were too _____
NOUN ADJECTIVE

to go skiing, so we just went back to the hotel and took a/an

_____. On the last day, the _____ came out and
NOUN NOUN

melted all the snow. Dad's face turned as red as a/an _____.
NOUN

Next year, Mom says we're going someplace warm. She's already

shopping for a new _____!
NOUN

MAD LIBS® is fun to play with friends, but you can also play it by yourself! To begin with, DO NOT look at the story on the page below. Fill in the blanks on this page with the words called for. Then, using the words you have selected, fill in the blank spaces in the story.

Now you've created your own hilarious MAD LIBS® game!

SUPERNANNY

NOUN_____

NOUN_____

CELEBRITY (FEMALE) _____

PLURAL NOUN_____

PLURAL NOUN_____

ADJECTIVE _____

ADJECTIVE _____

ADJECTIVE _____

NOUN_____

A PLACE_____

PLURAL NOUN_____

ADJECTIVE _____

NOUN_____

NOUN_____

ADJECTIVE _____

MAD LIBS®

SUPERNANNY

Television's newest _____ can get the most difficult
                          NOUN

_____ to overcome problems that have plagued
     NOUN

parents since the beginning of time. In each episode of *Supernanny*,

_____ works with children to correct their bad
CELEBRITY (FEMALE)

_____. She begins by explaining that she'd like them
  PLURAL NOUN

to follow some new _____. Then she proceeds to
                        PLURAL NOUN

reward _____ behavior and punish _____
         ADJECTIVE   ADJECTIVE

behavior. One _____ punishment is a short time-out
                  ADJECTIVE

on the "Naughty _____" or, for older children, in the
                     NOUN

"Naughty _____"—a place without _____
            A PLACE   PLURAL NOUN

or TV. The children's behavior grows more _____ with
                                               ADJECTIVE

each passing day, and eventually the desired _____ is
                                                  NOUN

achieved! *Supernanny* is ridding the world of behavioral dysfunction,

one _____ at a time. Too bad our _____ parents
      NOUN   ADJECTIVE

missed the cut and we turned out this way!

MAD LIBS® is fun to play with friends, but you can also play it by yourself! To begin with, DO NOT look at the story on the page below. Fill in the blanks on this page with the words called for. Then, using the words you have selected, fill in the blank spaces in the story.

Now you've created your own hilarious MAD LIBS® game!

CASE HISTORY: CONTROLLING MOTHER

VERB (PAST TENSE) _____

NOUN _____

ADJECTIVE _____

NOUN _____

ADJECTIVE _____

PLURAL NOUN _____

ADJECTIVE _____

NOUN _____

NOUN _____

PART OF THE BODY _____

ADJECTIVE _____

NOUN _____

MAD LIBS
CASE HISTORY:
CONTROLLING MOTHER

Agrippina _____ from A.D. 15 to A.D. 59. She
              VERB (PAST TENSE)

was clearly one of history's first "Controlling Mothers" because she

was always telling little Nero how to run the _____.
                                                  NOUN

As he matured, Nero became _____ and decided to
                             ADJECTIVE

have his mother moved to a/an _____ far away. But
                             NOUN

this didn't stop Agrippina's _____ ways, so Nero
                             ADJECTIVE

employed more extreme _____ to get rid of her. First
                          PLURAL NOUN

he tried poison, but it didn't work because she was _____
                                         ADJECTIVE

enough to take a/an _____ beforehand. Next, he tried
                        NOUN

to rig the _____ in her bedchamber to fall on her
                 NOUN

_____ while she slept, but that never works. Growing
PART OF THE BODY

desperate, he sent her out to sea in a/an _____
                                         ADJECTIVE

boat with a leaky _____, but she swam to safety.
                         NOUN

Nero finally gave up and became an actor, which those of us with

controlling mothers know is about all you can really do . . . .

MAD LIBS® is fun to play with friends, but you can also play it by yourself! To begin with, DO NOT look at the story on the page below. Fill in the blanks on this page with the words called for. Then, using the words you have selected, fill in the blank spaces in the story.

Now you've created your own hilarious MAD LIBS® game!

LIFE COACHING

NOUN_____

NOUN_____

NOUN_____

PLURAL NOUN_____

NOUN_____

NOUN_____

ADJECTIVE _____

NOUN_____

NOUN_____

VERB ENDING IN "ING"_____

ADJECTIVE _____

ADVERB _____

NOUN_____

PLURAL NOUN_____

NOUN_____

PLURAL NOUN_____

MAD LIBS
LIFE COACHING

Coaching is a partnership between a/an _____ and
NOUN

a/an _____ that is designed to help a dysfunctional
NOUN

young _____ reach his or her _____. It
NOUN PLURAL NOUN

is a step-by-_____ process that creates clarity and
NOUN

_____-filled moments. Here are some of the mental,
NOUN

emotional, and _____ benefits of coaching:
ADJECTIVE

• Discovering your inner _____ and allowing it to play
NOUN

• Recovering from a traumatic _____
NOUN

• Learning the art of "_____"
VERB ENDING IN "ING"

• Learning how to change _____ thinking
ADJECTIVE

• Learning how to protect yourself _____
ADVERB

The relationship between a/an _____ and a coach
NOUN

transforms _____. Too bad it costs more money than
PLURAL NOUN

you can shake a/an _____ at. Maybe you could try
NOUN

squeezing one of those nice stress _____ instead?
PLURAL NOUN

MAD LIBS® is fun to play with friends, but you can also play it by yourself! To begin with, DO NOT look at the story on the page below. Fill in the blanks on this page with the words called for. Then, using the words you have selected, fill in the blank spaces in the story.

Now you've created your own hilarious MAD LIBS® game!

DATING AFTER DIVORCE

VERB _____

NUMBER_____

ADJECTIVE _____

ADJECTIVE _____

ADJECTIVE _____

PLURAL NOUN_____

NOUN_____

PART OF THE BODY _____

PLURAL NOUN_____

NOUN_____

PLURAL NOUN_____

NOUN_____

VERB ENDING IN "ING"_____

ADJECTIVE _____

NOUN_____

MAD LIBS
DATING AFTER DIVORCE

It's been a few months since the divorce and you're ready to

_____ again. Whether you're forty or _____,
        VERB   NUMBER

dating might feel completely _____. Here are a few
                                      ADJECTIVE

tips to help you ease back into the _____ scene:
                                            ADJECTIVE

1. Don't try to look too _____. If you are fifty
                                  ADJECTIVE

    _____ or older, do not walk into a/an _____
     PLURAL NOUN   NOUN

    club frequented by nineteen-year-olds. You will stand out like a

    sore _____.
          PART OF THE BODY

2. Keep _____ short. It creates a sense of mystery.
          PLURAL NOUN

3. Do not, under any circumstances, talk about your ex-_____.
                                                            NOUN

4. Explore new _____. Consider using a/an _____
                 PLURAL NOUN   NOUN

    agency or visiting a/an _____ Web site. It might
                              VERB ENDING IN "ING"

    sound _____, but anything is worth trying at
            ADJECTIVE

    least once, right? Now get out there and find yourself that new

    _____ . . . or at least a new dog!
          NOUN